P R O M S

THE BBC PRESENTS
THE 97TH SEASON OF
HENRY WOOD PROMENADE
CONCERTS

ROYAL ALBERT HALL
19 JULY - 14 SEPTEMBER
1991

Member of the British Arts Festivals Association

Front and back cover photographs: Alex von Koettlitz

C O N T E N T S

Published by
BBC Concerts Publications
Editorial Office: Room 330,
16 Langham Street, London W1A 1AA
Distributed by BBC Books, a division of
BBC Enterprises Ltd, 80 Wood Lane,
London W12 0TT
© BBC 1991. ISBN 0–563–40966–5
Design: John Bury
Advertising: Rhona Lyle
Printed by Jarrold & Sons Ltd, Norwich

BP's latest refinery.

We're helping to refine Britain's natural reserves of musical talent through our sponsorship programme.

For all our tomorrows.

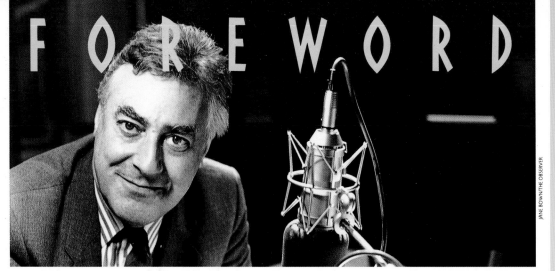

FOREWORD

John Drummond CBE
Controller, Radio 3

Nigel Wilkinson
Senior Proms Producer

Martin Cotton
*Chief Producer,
BBC Symphony Orchestra*

Nicola Goold
Press Officer

Ann Richards
Marketing Assistant

Graham Wood
Press Assistant

Henrietta Smythe
Proms Planning Assistant

Elizabeth Russell
Assistant, Concerts Finance

George Hall
Editor

Karen Cardy
Publications Organiser

Lindsay Kemp
Publications Assistant

MAYBE IT IS JUST MY AGE, but the years seem to go by at ever-increasing speed. The blazing summer and record Prom season of 1990 seem only yesterday – yet here we are with a new season, the sixth for which I have been responsible and the fifth for which I have planned the programmes. I'm sure that it's a good thing that one person should be responsible for the overall planning, but everyone knows that the days of artistic dictatorship are long since over. Now things happen through co-operation and joint planning, so, in the strictest sense, these are *our* programmes, made by those who plan and those who perform.

It is our policy to present mixed programmes, juxtaposing the new or the not so well known with the very familiar, so as to extend the knowledge and understanding of the audience. It is a deliberate decision to invite orchestras not only from outside London, but from overseas: we believe this gives the Promenade Concerts a truly international flavour. Conductors new to the Proms and young soloists are also part of the plan – it is a valuable experience for them to perform in such a warm and enthusiastic atmosphere, and is also a real challenge, especially for singers.

The absence of an overall theme this year is a reflection of our growing belief in the need to programme the widest range of music. Themes help to focus the mind, but they are not really essential. The past two 'themeless' seasons have proved more attractive to audiences than the two 'themed' ones that preceded them. Last year, we reached 86% average attendance (so much for those who say you cannot do anything in London in the month of August!).

It is also a deliberate decision once again to perform all the concerts in the Royal Albert Hall. This has meant that some small-scale elements have had to be excluded, but last year some of the late-night concerts drew audiences so much bigger than would have been possible in churches that I thought the change justified. The Royal Albert Hall has a splendid atmosphere, and its basic architecture means that members of the audience are conscious of each other and brought very close to the performers as well, creating a collective mood which is quite infectious.

I don't think it is at all surprising that so many people have come to love music through the Proms. I have clear memories of my own teenage visits, rushing to the rail to get close to the presence of great artists. I shall never forget standing about ten feet away from Kathleen Ferrier on one of her last appearances, radiating that intense joy in music that none of us who heard her can forget. The memory of that experience has never

left me. In many ways the Proms are the best place to hear music for the first time, as the sense of enjoyment so clearly outweighs that sense of duty which can infect concerts in other places.

And yet there remains one element which constantly disappoints me, and indeed many other people who would like to attend the concerts. That is the frequently sparse occupancy of the privately owned seats. It seems to me unreasonable that we should be turning away willing concert-goers when so many good seats remain empty. I quite understand that the private seat and box holders may have acquired their seats for some purpose other than music: tennis, boxing or whatever. But if they are not prepared to use them, why can they not return them to the Hall, and make them available to people who *do* want to attend – especially since they would gain financially by doing so?

Another of our policies has been to keep seat prices at an affordable level. This year there is a slight increase, especially for one or two major international nights, but the general level is well below that charged by the London orchestras on very ordinary nights in other halls. Inevitably, people have suggested that the BBC is not maximising its income to the fullest. I have to point out that there are many people in our society who cannot afford everything they would like, even if some of our critics have never met them. I feel a strong sense of con-

tinuity between the generations; I want parents to bring their children, and young people to feel they can come – and not only occasionally. If the BBC is seen to be subsidising musical life in this country, then that is something we have done for more than sixty years with – in my view – remarkable results.

This year there are nine orchestras and a chorus from abroad. Pride of place must surely go to the Berlin Philharmonic, making its first Prom appearance, with its new Principal Conductor, Claudio Abbado, in a Bank Holiday concert. Even at a higher price than usual, this should prove attractive, for in addition to this great orchestra there are two outstanding soloists: Cheryl Studer, making her Prom debut, and the pianist Alfred Brendel. Abbado – a relatively infrequent visitor to Britain these days – in fact comes twice to the Proms. As well as the Berlin Philharmonic, he brings his Vienna-based Gustav Mahler Jugendorchester. Its slightly older counterpart – the European Community Youth Orchestra – returns, this time under the baton of Vladimir Ashkenazy. Sir Colin Davis, always a welcome visitor, is to conduct one of Europe's oldest and most outstanding ensembles, the Dresden Staatskapelle, better known on this side of the continent for recordings than from concert appearances. There is a return visit from the Boston Symphony Orchestra, with its Principal Conductor, Seiji Ozawa, and a welcome reappearance of the Orchestre de Paris under their new conductor, Semyon Bychkov.

I always like the Proms to reflect the work of other radio symphony orchestras, and this year it is the turn of Finland. Their orchestra is conducted by Jukka-Pekka Saraste, and brings two well-known young Finnish soloists: Karita Mattila and Olli Mustonen. Two chamber orchestras are both first-time visitors: the Norwegian Chamber Orchestra, directed by Iona Brown (herself no stranger to the Proms), and the Orpheus Chamber Orchestra from New York, a conductorless ensemble of the highest quality. The overseas list is completed by – for the first time – a choir from the Soviet Union which, as well as appearing with Gennady

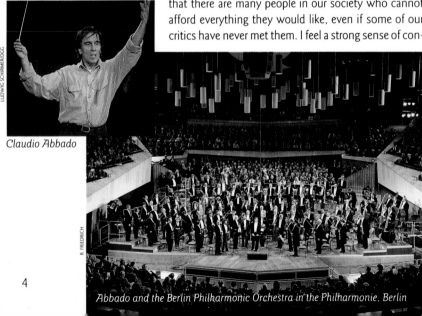

Claudio Abbado

Abbado and the Berlin Philharmonic Orchestra in the Philharmonie, Berlin

Rozhdestvensky in a little-known but splendid Dvořák work, will have a late-night concert all of its own.

Then there are the anniversaries. Every year the Proms include a large number of works by Mozart. In his bicentenary year we have two operas that work particularly well in the concert hall: Glyndebourne will be bringing *La clemenza di Tito*, and Welsh National Opera a preview of their new staging of *Idomeneo*. A total of 17 Mozart works are included in the season – a wide selection but by no means too much for a composer who is, in my view, impossible to hear too often.

This year also sees the centenary of the birth of Prokofiev. The high point for the Proms is the first performance here in Russian of his opera *The Fiery Angel*, which also marks the final appearance at the Proms of Edward Downes as Principal Conductor of the BBC Philharmonic, for which he has done so much. Prokofiev features in a number of other programmes, notably when Dame Judi Dench narrates *Peter and the Wolf* in a concert for young people on a Sunday afternoon. (Following last year's successful performance of *Noye's Fludde*, a Children's Prom seemed a new 'tradition' that we would be happy to encourage.)

Our other celebrations include the 150th anniversary of Dvořák's birth, the centenary of Arthur Bliss, the sixtieth birthday of Malcolm Williamson and the seventieth of Malcolm Arnold. The newly renamed Royal Scottish National Orchestra will make a centenary appearance under their long-time conductor Sir Alexander Gibson, and the great work done by Libor Pešek will be reflected in two concerts from the Royal Liverpool Philharmonic Orchestra. Simon Rattle's City of Birmingham Symphony Orchestra bring to the Proms for the first time the great violinist Gidon Kremer, while the Bournemouth Symphony Orchestra and the London Symphony Orchestra commemorate Leonard Bernstein. The other London orchestras' appearances notably include a performance of Beethoven's Ninth Symphony by Klaus Tennstedt; having failed to achieve this two years ago, through illness, we have high hopes for this year.

It has always been one of the most important functions of the Proms to present opportunities for new music to be heard by a very wide audience, and this season there are a number of commissions and first performances. In addition to the BBC's own commissions – from Hugh Wood, Martin Dalby, Nicholas Maw, Peter Paul Nash and Martin Butler – there will be world premieres of works by Witold Lutoslawski and Mark-Anthony Turnage, and a UK premiere for Sir Michael Tippett. Most of these will be performed by the BBC's own orchestras. Collectively, it seems to me, they have never been in better shape, and the range of their programmes, together with the quality of their playing, provide a total justification of their continuing role at the centre of music in this country.

Tippett's *Byzantium* will be included in one of the programmes to be conducted by the BBC Symphony Orchestra's Chief Conductor, Andrew Davis. It would be wrong of me not to refer to the great contribution that he is making to the musical life of this country in his combined roles as Chief Conductor of the BBC Symphony Orchestra and Musical Director of Glyndebourne Festival Opera. This season he conducts the First Night and the Last Night, the Glyndebourne visit and three other concerts. He seems to me to have stepped comfortably into the shoes of his great predecessors Sir Henry Wood, Sir Adrian Boult and Sir John Pritchard.

A last word about this Guide itself: with one hundred thousand copies sold each year, it is the largest-selling music publication in the world – yet another example of the way in which the BBC reaches out to a wide audience and makes an unrivalled contribution to European music. I hope you will find it not only a useful introduction to the season but a pleasure in itself.

We all look forward to you joining us, in the Hall or on radio or television, for what we hope will be another record-breaking season.

John Drummond

The Orpheus Chamber Orchestra

Seiji Ozawa and the Boston Symphony Orchestra

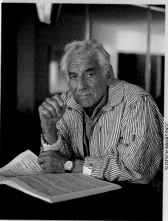
Leonard Bernstein (1918–90)

In 1853, Rubinstein created 'Melody in F'..

...and in Halifax, a building society was created, destined to become the world's Nº 1.

Scotch™
Videocassettes

FROM ONE QUALITY PERFORMANCE TO ANOTHER. GUARANTEED FOR LIFE.

3M Memory Technologies and Consumer Products Division

3M

ENDGAMES

David Cox discusses the evolution of the Last Night and its rituals

AUDIENCE INVOLVEMENT. End-of-season letting-down-of-hair. When did this start? How did it become what it now is?

According to Isobel Baillie, a veteran Prom singer born the same year as the Proms, there was very little audience participation at all in Henry Wood's time, and it was Malcolm Sargent who started all the Last Night business. Nevertheless, in the smaller space of the Queen's Hall, where control was easier than in the vast Albert Hall, Wood certainly allowed some Last Night audience involvement, as he tells us in *My Life of Music*:

> 'They stamp their feet in time to the hornpipe — that is, until I whip up the orchestra in a fierce *accelerando* which leaves behind all those whose stamping technique is not of the very first quality. I like to win by two bars, if possible ... It is good fun, and I enjoy it as much as they. When it comes to the singing of *Rule, Britannia!* we reach a climax that only Britons can reach, and I realise I can be nowhere in the world but in my native England'.

For him (strangely?) this was 'the epitome of the Proms' — a feeling no doubt linked to the early character of the series, when it was normal for serious and wide-ranging programmes to be diluted with light, popular items.

Wood's *Fantasia on British Sea-Songs* (to which the above quotation refers) was composed for a concert in 1905 to celebrate the centenary of Nelson's victory at Trafalgar, and it became an immediate success at the Proms. Like other particularly successful Last Night items, it stuck. One season, to test the audience, Wood omitted it. The volume of complaints was so great that he resolved never to do so again. In all, he included it in nearly forty seasons — and it has continued since his death, despite occasional attempts to abolish it.

Earlier, in 1901, Elgar's *Pomp and Circumstance Marches* Nos. 1 and 2 had enjoyed great success — especially No. 1, with the middle tune that became *Land of Hope and Glory*. Clara Butt sang the song ver-

ALEX VON KOETTLITZ

Sir Henry Wood conducting a Prom at the Royal Albert Hall in 1944

Dame Clara Butt as Britannia (1919)

sion the year after, which quickly took on the status of a second national anthem. Elgar also used the tune in his *Coronation Ode* for Edward VII, and he made it known that it was the King himself who had first suggested that words should be set to it. The poet Arthur Benson wrote the words of both the song and the ode, with a different emphasis in the latter:

> Land of Hope and Glory, Mother of the free,
> How may we extol thee who are born of thee?
> Truth and Right and Freedom, each a holy gem,
> Stars of solemn brightness, weave thy diadem.

But the tune in itself is far from pompous and heroic. As the critic Ernest Newman pointed out at the time, 'it is dignified in just the right kind of way in its proper place in the march', and 'is married to the words much against its own will'. Was it deliberately that Elgar, in the march, put the middle tune in a key convenient for singing? Did Wood in his time allow a 'singalong' when the march was played? Evidence for that, one way or the other, is hard to come by. The words of *Land of Hope and Glory* were not always printed in the programme of the concert, as they are now.

The other Last Night item which stuck was Parry's *Jerusalem*, first introduced by Sargent in 1953, for audience and orchestra, in the version orchestrated by Elgar for the Leeds Festival of 1922. Parry had set William Blake's words in 1916 at the suggestion of the poet Robert Bridges, who wanted it for performance in London at a meeting of the 'Fight for Right' movement in Queen's Hall. It was later associated with the 'Votes for Women' campaign, then taken up by the Federation of Music Competition Festivals and by the Federation of Women's Institutes – to say nothing of its widespread use in schools.

Blake's poetic imagery easily lends itself to a wide variety of interpretations, sometimes bizarre; but here the idealism which has been hitched upon so variously is made clear through the last part of his long poem *Jerusalem* (from which the words of the song itself are *not*, in fact, taken). The building of Jerusalem was for

9

'To Annihilate the Self-hood', one of Blake's etchings to his poem 'Milton' (1804–8), to which the words of the song Jerusalem form part of the Preface

Sir Malcolm Sargent conducting the Last Night of the 1954 season

Blake a vast pantheistic conception in which all forms of existence – human, animal, tree, metal, earth, stone – become one in the Life of Immortality. (No doubt this takes 'Fight for Right' and 'Votes for Women' in its stride!)

Parry's *Jerusalem*, in 1953, was the final item of a revised Last Night programme in which – against Sargent's advice – Wood's *Fantasia on British Sea-Songs* had been omitted. The BBC's then Head of Music, Maurice Johnstone, wrote: 'Its jingoism is out of date, and latterly its vestige of musicality has been destroyed by an enthusiastic but unthinking section of the audience'. He could hardly have known what strong feelings would be aroused among the Promenaders – the protests, the banners, the Prom hoardings defaced with 'WE WANT SEA SONGS' painted in black across them, and the press giving all of it wide coverage. Eventually, honour was more or less satisfied on both sides, and the *Sea-Songs* were played as a planned encore. The following season they were back in place. At the same time, Sargent was being accused of 'playing down to the audience' on the Last Nights, and of encouraging hysteria and exhibitionism which went beyond what he could control.

The next Last Night rumpus was in 1969, when the BBC's Music Controller, William Glock, in his reshaping of the Proms, omitted *Pomp and Circumstance* No. 1, with *Land of Hope and Glory*. Again, without success. There was public outcry, taken up by the press – even more intensely than before, because television had by then become involved in the Last Night. Colin Davis, Chief Conductor of the BBC Symphony Orchestra, was reported as saying what many others had said before – that 'jingoism, patriotic flag-waving and exhibitionism' were out of date. Glock, over the next three seasons, tried to change the pattern by inviting three well-known composers – Malcolm Arnold, Malcolm Williamson and Gordon Crosse – each to write a work involving the audience. Each was an imaginative experiment, but none found a lasting place.

During Sargent's reign an abbreviated version of the *Sea-Songs* became standard, ending with his own arrangement of *Rule, Britannia!*. Sargent also established the custom of the conductor's speech – which Wood would have found a repellent idea. With Sargent's illness and death in 1967, Colin Davis bravely took on the Last Night up to 1971. Thereafter it has been in the hands of various conductors, each of whom has reacted to the challenge in his own way. They have included Norman Del Mar, who reintroduced the complete version of the *Sea-Songs*; James Loughran, who added *Auld Lang Syne*; Sir John Pritchard, giving a personal and moving speech shortly before his death; and Andrew Davis, the BBC Symphony Orchestra's present conductor, whose cheerful and committed Last Night control worked well in 1988 and 1990.

*   *   *   *   *

So what are the pros and cons of the Last Night as it now stands?

First the cons. It's an unworthy end to a distinguished series of concerts. The behaviour of certain elements of the audience – with popping balloons, slogans, unmusical sound-intrusions – is annoying for the main audience and for listeners and viewers at home and abroad. The exuberance of young Promenaders often exceeds reasonable bounds, made worse by the television presence. Wood's *Fantasia on British Sea-Songs* is, musically, not a sufficiently interesting work. The stamping game in the Hornpipe is childish and absurd. The words of *Land of Hope and Glory* and *Rule, Britannia!* belong to our seafaring past, at the height of imperialism, when we depended on the navy for our island safety. Patriotic flag-waving suggests jingoism, belligerent nationalism. The Last Night has for long been in a rut and has become a meaningless, unchanging ritual.

And the pros. Wood certainly felt that some form of

relaxed enjoyment was appropriate at the end of so much concentrated listening. (But, just as he disliked Sargent's flamboyant style of conducting, so he would certainly also have disliked Sargent's shaping of the Last Night, which we have inherited.) Regarding the fixed favourites: *Land of Hope and Glory*, the *Sea-Songs* and *Rule, Britannia!* are enjoyed because they're good tunes (*Tom Bowling* especially), *not* because of their words. 'Wider still and wider shall thy bounds be set' might conceivably be reinterpreted as extending the bounds of understanding between the different nations of the world. As for the verbal images of *Rule, Britannia!*, they are so exaggerated and self-satirising ('When Britain first at Heaven's command / Arose from out the azure main, *etc.*) that even in the eighteenth century they must have been taken with a large amount of salt (or brine). If patriotic feeling is involved today, it must be remembered that there are two kinds of patriotism: one narrowly and aggressively nationalistic, the other altruistic – concerned with fellowship, neighbourliness, working together as a community, and with the natural feelings of love and loyalty one has for the land of one's birth.

As a people, we may like to express a feeling of unity through ceremony, often on a lavish scale. But, surely, the Last Night audience in the Albert Hall can scarcely be described as narrowly nationalistic. The flags of many countries can be seen among the throng. The atmosphere is more akin to that of an end-of-term party at which people gather round a piano and sing well-known songs purely for enjoyment. The piano has become an orchestra, the scale immensely magnified, and the songs may be from any period of our history.

The regular ingredients of the Last Night *could* change, or be added to, if other things were found which proved immediately successful (as *Jerusalem* did in 1953). The key is enjoyment. The first part of the concert is of a more serious nature, and is quietly and attentively listened to; the occasion as a whole can still be a worthy and friendly end to a great and friendly series of concerts.

Making up buttonholes for the chorus, orchestra and conductor

Variations on a theme by Mordaunt-Short

A theme featuring our new Series 3 loudspeaker systems.

A theme of innovation. A theme of excellence.

"Damnably impressive" said Hi-Fi Review of our MS3.30.

"Likely to set new standards of production quality" said What Hi-Fi? of our MS3.10.

Each Series 3 speaker takes as its theme the need to retain the integrity of the music.

It seems with some success.

Mordaunt-Short

CLOSER TO PERFECTION

Unit A1, Hazleton Industrial Park,
Lakesmere Road, Horndean, Portsmouth,
Hampshire PO8 9JU Great Britain.

Write or 'phone for a brochure and details of your nearest dealer.

THE SPAIN JUST WAITING TO BE TASTED.

RIOJA WINES

THESE FINE, DISTINCTIVE OAK AGED RED WINES
FROM THE NORTH HAVE ESTABLISHED SPAIN ON THE WINE LISTS
OF THE WORLD'S BEST RESTAURANTS.

CAVA WINES

THE LIGHT AND FRAGRANT SPARKLING WINES OF SPAIN
BRING A LIVELINESS TO ANY OCCASION.

PENEDÉS WINES

THE ELEGANT, FRUITY, DRY WHITE WINES OF PENEDÉS
ARE NOW WELL ESTABLISHED AMONG
THE LEADING WHITE WINES OF THE WORLD.

NAVARRA WINES

THIS HISTORIC KINGDOM PRODUCES PLEASING RED WINES
WHICH, WHEN AGED IN OAK,
SHOW A DELIGHTFUL AND SUBTLE ELEGANCE.

THESE ARE JUST A FEW OF THE CONSISTENTLY GOOD
QUALITY WINES FROM SPAIN THAT YOU CAN TASTE TODAY.

WINES FROM SPAIN, 66 CHILTERN STREET, LONDON W1M 1PR.

IMAGES OF RECONCILIATION

Andrew Huth *introduces Mozart's* Idomeneo *and* La clemenza di Tito, *and offers some bicentenary reflections*

Title-page of the score of
Idomeneo *in Mozart's hand*

AS OUR DESCENDANTS PREPARE to commemorate the tercentenary of Mozart's death in the year 2091, what will they make of our own bicentenary celebrations? When they have discounted some of 1991's sillier examples of commercial exploitation, will they sympathise with our attitudes to the composer? Or will they, perhaps, look back in amazement at our lack of taste, our failure of understanding? It seems impossible. Yet no-one in 1791 or 1891 could possibly have foreseen the position that Mozart now holds in our lives, and we, equally, find it hard to understand the view of Mozart that generally prevailed for the century-and-a-half following his death.

Mozart has never had to be rescued from total oblivion, of course. Although for a long time only a small proportion of the music he wrote was regularly played in public, there were always plenty of people (generally professional musicians) who worshipped him without reserve. But for the majority, Mozart came to be seen as no more than a composer of rococo prettiness or, hardly more sympathetically, as an elegant predecessor of the mighty Beethoven. At worst, he was sentimentalised; otherwise, he was just not quite good enough. Here, for example, is Queen Victoria, a cultured music-lover, writing to her eldest daughter in 1860: 'I was much amused to see your account of the musical tastes of the family. I can't understand their not admiring Meyerbeer, and Mendelssohn and Weber; Mozart I am not always quite so fond of, as I think the instrumentation so poor (it was so in those days)'.

One positive result of the cultural fragmentation of our own days has been to sharpen our historical awareness. We have turned away from an attitude which saw musical history in terms of a progress where succeeding generations built upon the work of their predecessors in an unbroken line of development to achieve ever greater

masterworks. All styles, we feel, must be allowed their own validity, irrespective of where they come from or where they lead to. The Viennese Classical style of the late eighteenth century, however – the style of Haydn, Mozart and Beethoven – will always be regarded as a peak of musical civilisation, where intellectual rigour achieved a perfect balance with consummate beauty.

No two works have benefited more from the mid-twentieth-century reappraisal of Mozart than the operas *Idomeneo* and *La clemenza di Tito* ('The Clemency of Titus'). Mozart was commissioned to write *Idomeneo* for the Munich Carnival of 1781, and the dress rehearsal took place on 27 January, his twenty-fifth birthday. It was his coming of age as a musical dramatist. A number of works from the preceding few years had shown signs of a new richness, a deepening and broadening of conception, notably the E flat Piano Concerto K271 of 1777 and the Sinfonia Concertante K364 of 1779. But nothing in Mozart's earlier music announces the sustained expressive level of *Idomeneo*.

The libretto was prepared by the Salzburg Court Chaplain, the Abbé Giambattista Varesco, and tells of the rash vow of Idomeneo, King of Crete. On returning from the Trojan War he is overtaken by a storm and vows to sacrifice the first living being he encounters on dry land if Neptune will spare him from the waves. The first person he meets turns out to be his own son, Idamante. This story, with its Old-Testament echoes and its final resolution in the birth of a new order based on love, drew from Mozart an opera in which for the first time he was able to demonstrate everything he had learnt about music, drama and human nature.

In the preceding two decades, the so-called 'reform operas' of Gluck had again posed that perennial question of the primacy of words or music in opera. In his famous preface to *Alceste* (published in 1769), Gluck had attacked what he saw as the operatic abuses of the day and stressed that the music should always serve the poetry. Mozart himself, in a letter of 1782 concerning *The Seraglio*, put the other point of view: 'poetry should be the obedient daughter of the music'. But Mozart was a supreme operatic composer because he knew that the whole question was really an irrelevance. What counted above everything else was dramatic effectiveness. *Idomeneo* is remarkable for the way in which he balances recitative, arioso, aria and ensemble in the construction of great spans of music in which every detail, however striking in itself, serves the greater dramatic whole.

A number of letters survive which give us some insight into Mozart's practical approach. Early in November 1780 he travelled to Munich on his own while his father Leopold remained behind in Salzburg to act as an intermediary between his son and the somewhat touchy librettist. We learn that Mozart wished to suppress an aria that Varesco had intended for Idomeneo at the end of Act 2: 'Here it will be better to have a mere recitative, well supported by the instruments. For in this scene ... there will be so much noise and confusion on the stage that an aria at this point

Portrait of the Mozart family (Wolfgang and his sister Nannerl at the keyboard) by Johann Nepomuk della Croce (c1780)

Welsh National OPERA

IDOMENEO

Wolfgang Amadeus Mozart

NEW PRODUCTION

Conductor	Sir Charles Mackerras
Producer	Howard Davies
Designer	William Dudley
Idomeneo	Dennis O'Neill/
	Anthony Roden
Idamante	John Mark Ainsley
Ilia	Amanda Roocroft
Elettra	Suzanne Murphy
Arbace	Anthony Roden/tba
Voice of Neptune	Ashley Thorburn

Cardiff New Theatre	18, 21, 25 Sept
then on tour to	
Liverpool Empire Theatre	10 Oct
Birmingham Hippodrome	15 & 18 Oct
Swansea Grand Theatre	22 & 25 Oct
Oxford Apollo Theatre	5 & 8 Nov
Southampton Mayflower	12 & 15 Nov
Bristol Hippodrome	19 & 22 Nov
Plymouth Theatre Royal	28 Nov

Full prices and booking details from
WNO Marketing
John Street
Cardiff CF1 4SP
Tel (0222) 464666

would cut a poor figure — and moreover there is the thunderstorm, which is not likely to subside during Herr Raaff's aria, is it?' (Anton Raaff, who created the role of Idomeneo, was then a distinguished veteran of sixty-six). The most effective way out of difficulties created by the librettist was generally to cut. 'When you read through the scene, you will see that it obviously becomes limp and cold by the addition of an aria or duet, and very gênant for the other actors who must stand by doing nothing ...' The voice of the Oracle of Neptune in Act 3 gave Mozart a great deal of trouble. The answer, again, was to cut. 'If the speech of the ghost in *Hamlet* were not so long, it would be far more effective. It is quite easy to shorten the speech of the subterranean voice and it will gain thereby more than it will lose.'

Dramatic pacing is certainly one of the keys to operatic success; but there is far more to it than that. What raises the mature operas to their undisputed level is Mozart's supreme knowledge of the human heart in all its passions, strengths and weaknesses. This quality has long been recognised in *The Marriage of Figaro*, *Don Giovanni* and *Così fan tutte*, the three works written to quicksilver libretti by Lorenzo Da Ponte, but it is only in recent years that we have learned to see *Idomeneo* and *La clemenza di Tito* in the same light. It was for many years believed that these operas were examples of a genre which was moribund even in Mozart's day. *Opera seria* was thought of as a highly artificial confection, a courtly entertainment consisting of a procession of high-minded but lifeless figures who would bewail their sufferings in formal arias until all entanglements were resolved by the fortuitous appearance of some *deus ex machina*.

Whereas nineteenth-century art tended to move towards ever greater naturalism, the twentieth century has rediscovered the value of stylisation in art and the cathartic power of ritual. Not only have we learned to appreciate more sympathetically the conventions of eighteenth-century opera, but we have also become aware that Mozart's dramatic genius actually thrived on

these conventions, infusing them with often startling originality. The characters in *Idomeneo* are anything but lifeless. Within their heroic mould, they are real and passionate creations who speak to us directly. Their big set-piece arias arise naturally from the events on stage, and give further impetus to the development of the dramatic situations. A high point is reached early in Act 3, when the four principal characters come together for the first time in a quartet which is at the same time a musical miracle, a turning point in the drama, a laying-bare of their tangled relationships and a distillation of transfigured suffering.

Ten years passed between *Idomeneo* and *La clemenza di Tito*, a period which included the composition of almost all the music by which Mozart is now known and loved: the three Da Ponte operas, the great piano concertos and symphonies, the string quartets and quintets — a vast production which accounts for some 250 entries in the catalogue of his works.

By the middle of July 1791 Mozart had completed most of *The Magic Flute* and was beginning work on the *Requiem* when he received the commission to compose an opera for performance in Prague on the occasion of the coronation of the new Emperor Leopold II as King of Bohemia on 6 September. Time was desperately short; there could be no question of getting a new libretto. The Court poet Caterino Mazzolà recast the old and successful *La clemenza di Tito*, which Pietro Metastasio had written for Caldara in 1734, and which had been set by over a dozen other composers since then. The subject-matter, loosely drawn from Roman history, could hardly be simpler. Shortly after the accession of the Emperor Titus Flavius Vespasianus in 79 AD a conspiracy is hatched against his life by Vitellia (daughter of the former Emperor, Vitellius), who seduces the patrician Sextus into assassinating the Emperor and sharing the throne with her. The conspiracy fails, the guilty confess, and the opera ends in magnanimity and forgiveness.

This idealised and formalised portrait of Monarchy and Society was appropriate enough for a coronation, a

Unfinished portrait of Mozart by his brother-in-law Joseph Lange (1789?)

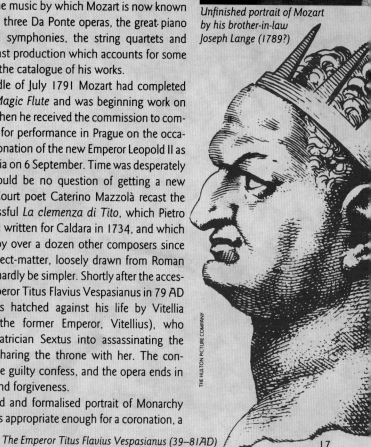

The Emperor Titus Flavius Vespasianus (39–81AD)

17

Pietro Metastasio (1698–1782), engraving by Paolo Caronni after Johann Steiner

An engraving showing festivities at the Coronation of Leopold II in Prague in 1791

Title-page of piano score of La clemenza di Tito, *Hamburg, c1795*

celebration of an *ancien régime* soon to be swept away by the turmoil of the French Revolution, but it is not the stuff of drama, let alone of tragedy. There is no sense of inexorable fate or of heroic confrontation with the inevitable, as in *Idomeneo*. But the characters in *La clemenza di Tito* are also enmeshed in conflicts of love and loyalty, and the lack of external action only throws the emphasis more firmly on their personal dilemmas.

The musical style of *La clemenza di Tito* relates it closely to the other great works of Mozart's final months. There are many echoes of the tender simplicity of *The Magic Flute*, as well as the common theme of reconciliation and understanding. The choral writing, especially in the Act 1 finale, anticipates the sombre drama of the *Requiem*, and the instrumental sound is frequently close to the mellow beauty of the Clarinet Concerto, Mozart's last major instrumental work. Indeed, two of the arias in *La clemenza di Tito* feature elaborate obbligato parts designed expressly for the clarinet virtuoso Anton Stadler, who travelled to Prague with Mozart, and for whom the concerto was written on Mozart's return to Vienna. But beyond such parallels and similarities, *La clemenza di Tito* exists in a world of its own: whether in the formal grandeur and brilliance of the overture, marches and choruses, or in the more intimate emotions of the principal arias and ensembles, there is a particular underlying mood and colouring, a grave, elegiac and luminous beauty unique in Mozart's music.

Three months after the first performance of *La clemenza di Tito* Mozart was dead. Joseph Haydn was in London when the news reached him. Distraught at the loss of his friend, and at the loss to music, he lamented, 'posterity will not see such a talent again in a hundred years'. Two hundred years have now passed, and we are still waiting.

Glyndebourne Festival Opera's semi-staged version of their new production of La clemenza di Tito *can be seen in Prom 44; Welsh National Opera bring* Idomeneo, *in a concert performance, to Prom 66*

PROKOFIEV TODAY

Christopher Palmer *assesses the appeal of Prokofiev and previews his opera* The Fiery Angel

N A *TIMES* PREVIEW of the RPO's winter Prokofiev series, Richard Morrison claimed that the growing popularity of Shostakovich was being counterbalanced by a gradual eclipse of Prokofiev, widely regarded for many years (though not necessarily by the Russians themselves) as the Soviet Union's premier composer. But is it true that Prokofiev is falling from popular grace? And if he is, why?

The key word is perhaps 'popular' in the sense of for, or of, the people. I do not think Prokofiev's appeal to a wide, and in this sense 'popular', audience has ever been in doubt, or ever will be. He has always been a music-lover's composer. Those who find him a problem tend to be rather the critics, the musicologists, those who attempt to sway public opinion and set fashionable trains-of-thought in motion, those whose response to music is more critical, intellectual and analytic than purely musical or music-loving. The 'problem' that these musicians have with Prokofiev is, frankly, that he is *not* a problem.

While Prokofiev's life was one of the most eventful and fascinating of any twentieth-century composer — far more so than Shostakovich's — his music *per se* is singularly simple and straightforward. In a sense — the sense that intellectual complexities play hardly any part in its scheme-of-things — there's actually very little to say about it, at least on a high-powered critico-intellectual level, and very little *has* been said, or written.

There is always a certain inbuilt critical resistance to composers who command a wide public following if, as in the case of Rimsky-Korsakov, their music is light on emotion and heavy on glitz and glamour; or if, like Prokofiev, they are deemed not to have contributed much to the evolutionary march of music, *ie* to have remained within the tonal orbit. Shostakovich did too, of course, but his music carries a much heavier emotional charge than Prokofiev's.

Ultimately, Prokofiev remained sublimely unaware of — or at least unexercised by — any contemporary 'crisis'

A scene from the Netherlands Opera production of The Fiery Angel *(June 1990), designed by Robert Israel and produced by Andrei Serban: Marilyn Zschau as Renata*

or 'Angst'. He found all the nurture he needed in Classicism and Russian nationalism; seminal figures like Debussy, Schoenberg, even Stravinsky (whose influence on Prokofiev is sporadic and superficial) might virtually never have existed as far as he was concerned.

When a twentieth-century composer writes unstudiedly simple and straightforward music of the kind with which Ernest Newman's 'plain man' (now less ceremoniously referred to as Joe Public) has minimal difficulty in coming to terms, that 'unstudiedly' implies a direct reflection or expression of the composer's uncomplicated nature and optimistic *Weltanschauung*. In 1962, when Stravinsky returned to Russia for the first time in nearly fifty years, he attended a reception in Moscow's Metropole Hotel given by Ekaterina Furtseva, the then Minister of Culture, to which selected Soviet composers — among them Shostakovich — were also invited. In response to an 'optimistic' remark by Stravinsky she advanced the somewhat — nay, highly — dubious proposition that 'all really great men are optimists'. Optimists! With Shostakovich sitting within earshot! What must he have thought in thus hearing his 'greatness' implicitly gainsaid? 'Great' composer he certainly was, but *optimistic*?

Here, he and Prokofiev were as chalk and cheese. Shostakovich deals with the mass grave and nuclear warfare in his music: he anathematises, monumentalises, immortalises, the unthinkable tragedy of the Soviet people under Stalin. His music may well be accounted one of the most devastating indictments of totalitarianism in our century. Now Prokofiev suffered all that, lived through all that, saw not only friends and colleagues but also his wife disappear into Stalin's prisons and labour-camps (the latter, unlike most of the former, came back to tell the tale). But there is nothing of all that in his music. His expressed view — and we, despite its Soviet context, have no reason to doubt its sincerity — was that the composer's duty was 'to serve his fellow men, to beautify human life and point the way to a radiant future'. Try telling that to Shostakovich. He would have been as bewildered as many Westerners have been by the fact that Prokofiev's 1939 *Ode to Stalin* (a.k.a. *Zdravitsa*) is not only one of his most attractive shorter works in general but contains one of his finest melodic inspirations in particular. However used we may be to devils getting the best tunes, we know *now* — admittedly with more certainty than Prokofiev can have realised *then* — that Stalin was

Portrait of Prokofiev (1934) by P. Konchalovsky

Prokofiev (left) with Shostakovich (centre) and Khachaturian, Moscow, 1945

It's events like these we help get off the ground.

Every year NatWest sponsor many Arts events. We encourage Theatre,
Opera, Ballet, Jazz Bands and Choral Societies.
It's a policy we're very proud of. And a policy we intend to continue.

♻ NatWest The Action Bank

the greatest mass-murderer in the history of the world. How can we be reconciled to such a work? *No problem* once we understand that the *Zdravitsa* has in its true being nothing to do with Stalin, however often his name may have been (no longer is, in the contemporary 'official' version) mentioned in the text. The music is not a representation of life under communism as it actually *was* – this is Shostakovich territory – but rather a vision, a mirage, of the utopia envisaged as an ideal before those who came to power perverted and corrupted and finally destroyed it.

Paradoxically the opera *The Fiery Angel*, the main focus of the BBC's Prokofiev centenary celebrations at the Proms, is the kind of subject one might reasonably have expected to appeal more to Shostakovich than Prokofiev. Its source was a long-short story by Valery Bryusov (1873–1924), an important figure in the Russian Symbolist movement, who marshalled some pretty heavy – not to say heady – artillery with which to assault 'bourgeois' sensibilities, including sexual mania, sado-masochism, black magic and the concept of woman as a source of poisonous evil. *The Fiery Angel* is set in sixteenth-century Germany, and treats of 'a devil who more than once appears to a young maiden in the form of a fiery spirit and tempts her to commit various sinful acts; of godless dealings in magic, astronomy and necromancy ... '. The subject is really religious hysteria at the time of the Spanish Inquisition, and the heroine is one of those ambivalent females, 'half saint, half whore, torn between the two extremes of sexual self-indulgence and religious self-denial' (Harlow Robinson).

One can easily imagine Shostakovich being attracted to such a subject – Renata and Lady Macbeth (of Mtsensk) are in many ways birds of a feather, at least in so far as their destructive relations with men are concerned – but Prokofiev? If Prokofiev is so much in love with life, light and joy, how can he encompass musically the powers of darkness? There is, after all, one episode in Act 2 of *The Fiery Angel* which seems to me one of the most frankly terrifying portrayals of horror in music. Renata uses black magic to summon her long-lost 'Angel' to her presence. Knocks on the wall indicate the approach of someone or something. The knocks grow more insistent: it seems 'he' is climbing the stairs. For one hysterical moment we expect to see the door open, but ... nothing. Ruprecht looks out – nobody. This amazing passage is like nothing else in Prokofiev, or in music. When Sviatoslav Richter heard it (in its Third Symphony context), he 'saw' a massive conflagration in the air with flakes of ash flying and whirling around. And it is not self-consciously diabolic or horrific any more than the best of Prokofiev's children's music – *Peter and the Wolf* and *Winter Bonfire* – is self-consciously simple or childlike. We have no sense of Prokofiev *trying* to do something special: he just *does* it, and it sounds completely right.

I make no idle mention of the children's music in this context, for it may provide the clue to the *Fiery Angel* phenomenon – 'phenomenon' in that it is hard enough to understand the appeal of the story to Prokofiev in the first place, much less his spectacular success in realising it. But 'children' can be readily swayed in either direction, black or white, good or evil: remember Quint and the two children in *The Turn of the Screw*. In 'adult' people convention and civilisation and education have so obscured natural reason that they are as incapable of appreciating – and therefore, in the case of composers, of expressing – true wickedness as they are of true goodness. But 'child'-people – by which term of course I do not mean people who are retarded but those, like Prokofiev, whose perceptions always retain the freshness and immediacy of childhood – can experience horror in close-up in the very presence of evil. Does this have something to do with the potency of *The Fiery Angel*? Its inspiration is at white heat almost from first to last: one imagines Prokofiev working on it – and the phrase is macabrely apposite – like one possessed.

In fact the *Fiery Angel* phenomenon is particularly, ghoulishly, meaningful today in the light of recent press concern about 'alleged ritual abuse' – *ie* Satan and sex, Satan and *child*-sex moreover, as in *The Fiery Angel*:

Netherlands Opera's The Fiery Angel

JAAP PIEPER

SOCIETY FOR CULTURAL RELATIONS WITH THE USSR

Valery Bryusov (1873–1924) during the 1890s

when the Angel or Devil — we are never quite sure which — first appeared to Renata she was seven, and when she was fifteen *she* seduced *him*. By Act 5, clearly the victim of diabolic possession, she is ready to seduce an entire convent and raise her hand against the Inquisitor himself — and this scene in its intensity, complexity and sheer intimidating grandeur is one of Prokofiev's most stunning *tours-de-force*.

Prokofiev never saw this much-cherished opera — he worked on it for some eight years, from 1919 to 1927 — produced on the stage in his lifetime. He never even heard a complete concert performance — Koussevitsky gave Act 2 in the spring of 1928 — yet when the stage premiere finally took place in 1955, two years after the composer's death, critical acclaim was enormous, and to this day the opera has never failed to grip audiences. The Third Symphony (based on the music of the *Angel*) is impressive enough, but once one has become familiar with the opera the symphony always thereafter sounds more like what it is — a 'symphonic suite from ... '. Ironically, though conductor Edward Downes has made his own translation of the libretto, the Prom performance will be the first in this country to be sung in Prokofiev's original Russian, which I'm convinced will reveal an unsuspected dimension of colour and intensity. And after all, not only is *The Fiery Angel* a magnificent achievement *per se*, it is also a milestone in Prokofiev's composing career. It was his last great fling as a maverick, a renegade, an apostle of the old pre-revolutionary order. Thereafter he settled down to the task of becoming a Russian composer New Style — *ie* a pro-Soviet. And what a splendid showing he made at that, too.

Edward Downes conducts a concert performance of The Fiery Angel *in Prom 41*

The final scene of The Fiery Angel in the Netherlands Opera production

JAAP PIEPER

Investigate...Contemplate...Appreciate...

THE NEW GROVE® is the ultimate source of information in the musical world. It is widely acclaimed for its scope, lucidity and unparalleled authority. Thousands of musicians, scholars and music-lovers refer to the pages of The New Grove for its full-length articles on literally every aspect of music.

To make the prospect of owning the 20-volume set even more attractive, we are currently offering a choice of either a FREE £120 voucher (to spend at either HMV, Blackwell's, Dillon's or Heffers) or 12 FREE CDs from the *Hyperion* catalogue. We urge you to act before the offer expires on 30 September 1991.

Moreover, in order to make The New Grove more easily affordable, you now have the chance to spread payment over 2 years*. Or, if you choose to purchase the books in one payment, you will receive a £110 discount.

For a free copy of our 28-page prospectus, and for further details of our special offer, just write to: Jonathan White, Grove's Dictionaries of Music, Macmillan Publishers Ltd, FREEPOST, 1 Melbourne Place, London WC2B 4LF.

Or call 071-379 4687 (fax 071-379 4980).

WIN A FREE 1992 PROMS SEASON TICKET

Call 071-379 4687 for a copy of The New Grove Quiz (comprising of 10 questions) and further details. Correct answers pulled out of the hat win a Proms Season ticket

*APR 22.1% A written statement of our terms of business may be obtained from the address above. **The New Grove** and **The New Grove Dictionary of Music and Musicians** are registered trademarks of Macmillan Publishers Ltd, London.

The New Grove Dictionary of Music and Musicians®

Edited by Stanley Sadie

HEIRS AND REBELS

Diana McVeagh *explores the diversity of the twentieth-century English composers whose music is heard at this year's Proms*

WHAT IS AND CAN BE an English School of Music? The question was Elgar's, posed in 1905 in his inaugural lecture as Peyton Professor at Birmingham University. He took the date 1880 as a starting-point for young native composers in relation to the music of the day; yet he bemoaned the want of inspiration in the many respectable and effective works composed since then. He called for 'something that shall grow out of our own soil, something broad, noble, chivalrous, healthy and above all, an out-of-door sort of spirit ... To arrive at this it will be necessary to throw over all imitation'. Carefully choosing an indefinite title for his lecture – 'A Future for English Music' – he went on: 'what THE future of English music may be, no man can say'.

Just as well! Only seven years later a man of the succeeding generation asked plaintively, 'who wants the English composer?', unappreciated at home and unknown abroad. It was a strange comment, for Elgar was then fifty-five and at the peak of his renown. But Vaughan Williams, speaking for the *young* English composer, could find no guidance in Elgar, who closed an epoch. For Vaughan Williams, folk song was 'the germ from which all musical developments ultimately spring'; and he recommended the young composer to find himself in his own community.

Britten, too, found his immediate past barren for his needs. In 1945 he declared his aim in *Peter Grimes* was 'to restore to the musical setting of the English language a brilliance, freedom and vitality that have been curiously rare since the death of Purcell'.

Elgar, Vaughan Williams and Britten: three native composers of undoubted stature. Each called for a return to his own definition of what was truly English. But each aroused plenty of controversy in his time. Despite the fact that many of Elgar's early admirers were German, his countrymen sometimes hugged him too possessively to their own hearts. Casals's playing of the Cello Concerto (Prom 29) was dubbed 'un-English', when it was probably his personality rather than his foreignness that seemed out of keeping, for the French Tortelier's interpretation of the same work is rated among the finest.

So, for this Proms season, when English twentieth-century works from *The Dream of Gerontius* to *Earth Dances* are being performed, it might once more be asked: what makes English music English?

Received opinion runs something like this. English music is lyrical or rugged, its melodies rounded, its harmonies consonant, or at least its dissonances diatonic. It is thoughtful rather than intellectual, mystical rather than rational, noble and ceremonial rather than brilliant. Rooted in the land and in the past, it is conservative, suspicious of radical, continental innovation, and of much opera. Under its contemplative flow, there runs a bitter-sweet melancholy. Such an attempted definition may do for some works, or even for part of some works. But it soon looks limited. If pressed, it begins to look tired and outworn, even with elements of caricature.

Elgar and Delius are often claimed as having a deep affinity with English landscape and poetry. Both took

Edward Elgar and Marco

much from Wagner – though Elgar's chromaticism is the more propulsive, Delius's the more sensuous and non-developing. Both men were long in maturing, and found themselves only in works composed at the turn of the century. But how opposed were their attitudes to the problem of finite life! Elgar's search for religious certainty in *The Dream of Gerontius* (Prom 1) could scarcely be further from the hedonism of Delius's *A Village Romeo and Juliet* (Prom 67). Elgar's old man is a seeker, Delius's adolescent lovers, so poignantly separated, can find peace only in nature's eternal renewal. The Paradise Garden is set on earth, Elgar's paradise is with the angels; Delius's river brought death, Elgar's lake the hope of redemption.

Delius and Elgar have more in common between *Paris* and *In the South* (Prom 9). Elgar's *Cockaigne* (Prom 67) of 1901, for all its dislocated street band, belongs to an old established world. By the time of his 'London' Symphony (Prom 54) Vaughan Williams had assimilated what he needed from Tudor church music and native folk song to create his new world, an assured agreement of style and substance. This was his practical answer to 'who wants the English composer?' The common chords, undulating cantabiles, austere climaxes, add up, paradoxically, to a deeper certainty than can be found in Elgar's First Symphony (Prom 3), whose opulent sounds veil a sensibility far more introverted than Vaughan Williams's.

Between Elgar's last big great work and Walton's first lay ten years. When Elgar heard Walton's Viola Concerto (Prom 18) he appeared to hate it. Is it possible,

Ralph Vaughan Williams in the Royal Army Medical Corps in 1915

however, that he recognised only too well how close it stood to his own Cello Concerto, how both shared that piercing lyricism that goes back to Dowland? Old men do not like contenders in their own sphere, and maybe it was a raw nerve, not lack of judgment, that prompted Elgar's outburst. Walton's *Belshazzar's Feast* (Prom 48) of 1931, however, is as far in spirit from Elgar's oratorios as could be: extrovert, dramatic, barbaric, with no Christian sentiment or edification. Much of that same driving rhythm impels Walton's First Symphony (Prom 49). He had told his publisher that he wished to return to the 'pure form of the Beethoven nine'. There is something in this symphony, too, of the ruthless power of Beethoven's Seventh, something also of the bardic Sibelius, that composer so loved by the English. Walton's compressed emotion is electrifying.

Only two years later, in 1937, came a work as spare as the Walton is massive. Wry, nervy, elegant, the *Variations on a Theme of Frank Bridge* (Prom 14) brought forward in Britten a composer who gave a new brilliance to English music. Foreign references abound: Rossini, Prokofiev, Stravinsky's *Apollon musagète*; but under the balletic gestures, the parodies, the masks, there sounds a voice clear and astonishingly sad.

About the same time another young composer was offering music from a temperament so bountiful and fecund that it occasionally risks incongruity. Tippett's Concerto for Double String Orchestra (Prom 49) shares with Vaughan Williams the debt to folk song and Tudor music – madrigals not church – and comes from a mind as supple and intricate as Vaughan Williams's was

The London Vaughan Williams knew: Regent Street c1910

Fritz (later Frederick) Delius in 1899

Walton in a portrait by Michael Ayrton (1948)

Benjamin Britten (centre) with Frank and Ethel Bridge (1937)

Michael Tippett in a portrait by Juliet Pannett (1958)

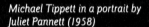

sturdy. Both composers place great value on human potential, which in Tippett's case found an apotheosis in *The Midsummer Marriage*. The exuberance of this world – the ornamental lyrical lines, the layered harmonies – is reflected in his Piano Concerto (Prom 17), together with the 'magic' sounds which give a mysterious new insight into man's relationship with nature.

An older piano concerto, of 1938, is the most backward-looking, but also the most glamorous, of these English works. Bliss, whose centenary falls this year, was commissioned to write his concerto (Prom 2) for Solomon to perform in New York, which meant, he thought, that it must be grand and Romantic. So it is; and he was possibly the only man in this country with the panache to have composed it (and how dashing that jazzy recapitulation sounds!).

By contrast, Frank Bridge's *Phantasm* (Prom 48), also for piano and orchestra, was for its time – 1931 – remarkably advanced, and reaches into areas of Expressionist feeling hardly explored in England. The potent atmosphere, shadowy yet obsessive, suggests a mind courageous enough to follow dark elusive hints, cogent enough to shape them surely. Bridge's music can be as sensuous as Delius and Bax, and his continuously-evolving thematic style makes for a vigorous and rapturous experience in *Enter Spring* (Prom 54). But his more radical music made little headway in pre-War England, and now, fifty years after his death, reparation is being made for his neglect.

For a period his name lived mostly in connection with his pupil Britten. If Britten shared with his teacher a willingness to learn from the continent, it was from different masters. Much of Britten's music is concerned with finding a balance between the conflicts within his own temperament, and the conflicts he faced in his position in English music. At the outbreak of war there could be no straight looking-back to his own inheritance. The *Sinfonia da Requiem* (Prom 24) was composed in the United States, and the peace of the final 'Requiem aeternam' is not an achieved state, but a precarious balance of limpid diatonic melody over contradicting harmonic centres. Needing to separate himself still further from the 'English' style, he worked through settings of French and Italian before coming again to English words. In the *Serenade* (Prom 50) this distancing produced a work of astonishing freshness and certainty. Britten's grip of each poem is such that he dares flatten speech-rhythms for atmospheric effect, or even to give the horn – not the voice – the emotional burden. In each song the pull between the rigorously controlled form and the fluent, beguiling voice is intense.

With his capacity for drama as well as lyricism, it was inevitable that Britten should turn to opera. The production of *Peter Grimes* in 1945 changed English music. Till then, opera had not been a strong native growth, but paradoxically *Peter Grimes* might be deemed Britten's most English work up to that time. It has a strong sense of locality – the cutting edge of the high single line that opens the first of the *Four Sea-*

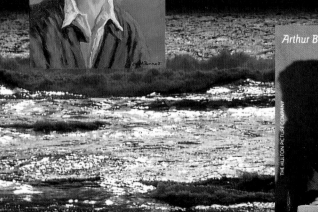

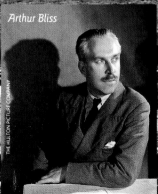

Arthur Bliss

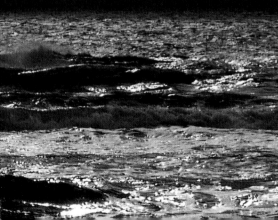

British Gas

AFTER THE ELECTRIC GUITAR, THE GAS VIOLIN?

Every year, thousands of talented youngsters will find their accompanist on the musical stage is British Gas. Because British Gas are backing a number of musical events across the country.

From the hugely successful Carl Flesch International Violin Competition, right across the musical calendar to major sponsorship of the National Youth Jazz Orchestra. So alongside the gas violin, we're hoping the jazz improvisations will lead to some new gas works. And that our Cathedral Classics with their organ solos will sound even better coming from the gas pipes.

British Gas. Supporting music in the community.

Interludes (Prom 3) comes straight off the North Sea. The idea of the tormented anti-hero and the conventions he half flouts, half wants to accept, is deeply embedded in the less attractive, hypocritical side of English small-town life, and provided Britten with a perfect challenge to his personal and technical bent.

Generally regarded as being outside the English national tradition is Lennox Berkeley. His Gallic virtues of economy, fluency and fastidiousness are often accounted for by his study with Nadia Boulanger, but more likely he knew his own temperament well enough to seek out the training best suited for it. His enchanting *Divertimento* (Prom 27) shares with Britten and Tippett a touch of neo-classicism, but has none of Britten's menace or Tippett's diffuseness. Berkeley's honed lyricism proves that lightness need not be facile or frivolous. Malcolm Arnold, seventy this year, stays popular thanks to his genial manner and skilful orchestration. His decisively tonal style can accommodate in his Guitar Concerto (Prom 2) the fetching kitsch tune in the first movement and an imaginative threnody in the second.

Listening to Robin Holloway's Horn Concerto (Prom 9), the world of Delius and Elgar seems as though Vaughan Williams had never happened. Here the wheel turns almost full circle, for Holloway's point of departure seems to have been German Lieder, and from there on to Wagner and Strauss – who were, after all, influences on those most 'English' composers Delius and Elgar. Holloway's music is another example of how the past can bear creative fruit: it has reopened nineteenth-century areas of expression, not in any reactionary way, but to assimilate them into a modern experience.

There is in any great composer some possibility of violence. How deeply covered it is will depend on the conventions of his society acting on his impulses. In some English music it is softened, or controlled, into melancholy. But it was present in Elgar, as a 'malign influence' in the Second Symphony. It makes for the royal fury of Vaughan Williams's Fourth Symphony. It is the spring of the action in *Peter Grimes*. In Birtwistle, who is fascinated by the great myths and legends that underpin the human psyche, it has assumed a greater significance. His *Earth Dances* (Prom 50) is as violent as Stravinsky's *Rite of Spring*. This is music of apparently startling primitivism. The formal and instrumental procedures are organised, but in the way of geological strata, so that long, drawn-out lines are cut across with crashing vertical chords. It works, as it were, on several planes, and on its own time-scale. If this is 'English' music, it is granite rather than Cotswold stone. It has immense power and energy. Birtwistle seems engaged in some awesome, even baleful, celebration. He has forged his own style in response to his own need in his own time. That, after all, is what Elgar, Vaughan Williams and Britten did. The right way for one was no use to the next. It seems there must be a time-lapse before the past can be used creatively. But with composers today as strong and individual as Holloway and Birtwistle, there will surely be a good future for English music.

Piano duettists Benjamin Britten (left) and Lennox Berkeley rehearsing a puppet play (1938)

Malcolm Arnold

Robin Holloway

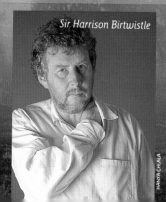

Sir Harrison Birtwistle

Gustav Holst (left) and Ralph Vaughan Williams walking during the 1920s (photograph taken by W.G. Whittaker)

David Osmond-Smith
*introduces two works
by Italy's leading composer,
Luciano Berio, to be heard
at this year's Proms*

BERIO HAS ALWAYS shown an affinity for the orchestra. Arriving as a student at the Milan Conservatory at the close of the Second World War, after an adolescence in which even the chance to hear a live orchestra was a rarity, he launched himself with the eagerness of one deprived into a study of the orchestral tradition. By the late 1950s his flair for handling complex orchestral sonorities was widely admired: and ever since it has been one of the most striking and attractive features of his music. But when a post-war composer writes for a symphony orchestra he has to enter into a dialogue: both with the instrumental resources that our ancestors put together to serve very different musical purposes and (just as interesting a

challenge) with the audiences that sustain the symphonic tradition. It is a dialogue that Berio evidently enjoys, and one that he has taken up repeatedly.

At the heart of the symphonic tradition lies an eminently democratic principle: music for the public concert-hall must offer something to all types of listener. It was with *Sinfonia*, written in 1968 for an orchestra containing amplified voices, that Berio confirmed his ability to respond to that challenge. For all its sophisticated games with Mahler's music, and Lévi-Strauss's words, *Sinfonia* made its impact with a direct, vivid style of writing that demanded no special skills, just an appetite for adventure. It was some years before Berio decided once again to turn to so open-handed a

VOICES IN THE ORCHESTRA

project, but in 1975 he started work on a successor to *Sinfonia, Coro*, which he completed in the following year.

Coro is a classic example of the pleasure that Berio takes in renewing well-established expectations. But instead of placing his singers as a choir standing behind, and accompanied by, the orchestra, Berio blends them together into a single enormous ensemble. Individual voices and instruments are paired, sitting side by side. The duets thus created are sometimes heard singly, but are so disposed about the stage that they can combine to create dialogues between chamber groups, or coalesce into a single, massive *tutti*.

But Berio was not content merely to find new uses for established resources. The materials articulated by this vast ensemble engage with traditions very different from those of the concert platform. From his student days on, one of Berio's abiding obsessions has been folk music – not as a relic of lost authenticity, but as an example of how simplicity and subtlety can be made to work together. In *Folk Songs* (1964) or *Voci* (1984) he built his own commentary around folk tunes. But *Coro* moves on to a more complex project. It sets a great variety of folk texts from around the world, many of them translated into English word-for-word so that they keep a rough, alien edge. Berio's music equally acknowledges a sense of distance. It sets up cross-fertilisations between a whole range of folk-techniques, but attempts neither pastiche nor extended quotation. The lively polyglot idiom that results is very much Berio's own.

Inventive reshaping is the hallmark of Berio's relationship to his own music as well. The revisiting of ideas explored in previous works is a natural part of any composer's development, but Berio is able to involve his listeners in the process in an unusually explicit way. This is because his experiences with electronic resources in the mid-1950s encouraged in him an enjoyment of complex sound organised in counterpointed layers. Transposing this approach into an instrumental sphere, he could thus revisit an already completed piece

and place it in quite new perspectives by adding round it further layers of material that might expand upon, contradict, or even obliterate his original 'text'. (The best-known examples of this are his *Sequenzas*, which he subsequently elaborated into *Chemins* by adding a surrounding ensemble.)

However, this expansion from a central core is an approach that can also form part of the initial process of composition. In *Points on the curve to find ...* (1974), Berio first established a toccata-like oscillating central line for solo piano (the 'curve' of the title) governed by a systematic rotation process that invites the ear constantly to explore new harmonic 'points' within its fixed resources. The surrounding ensemble uses this central line as a trampoline, bouncing off it in all directions to colonise new regions.

The exuberance and lucidity of *Points on the curve to find ...* made it one of the most accessible works from an experimental phase in Berio's development. Indeed, Berio soon conceived of using it as the core of a larger concerto for piano and orchestra. But with three major projects on hand in the late 1970s and early 1980s (*Coro*, followed by his two music-theatre works, *La vera storia* and *Un re in ascolto*), the execution of this idea was long deferred. When finally Berio took the matter up again in 1988, he had expanded into a richer and more allusive harmonic idiom, so that although *Points on the curve to find ...* had now become the central part of a triptych, called *Concerto II (Echoing Curves)*, it was itself the object of a process of commentary in which Berio reviewed his language of the mid-1970s in the light of the rich resources of the late 1980s. The layers of musical thought are distinguished spatially, with the original ensemble of *Points on the curve to find ...* at the centre of the stage around the solo piano, and a second ensemble set out around the periphery. Here Berio is engaged in dialogue not just with tradition, but with his own past.

Berio conducts Coro *and* Echoing Curves *in Prom 5*

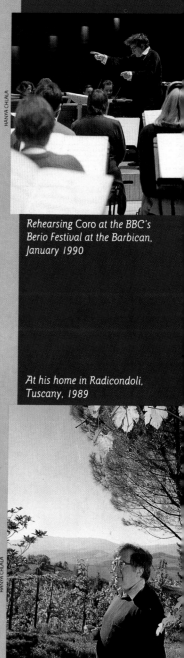

Rehearsing Coro *at the BBC's Berio Festival at the Barbican, January 1990*

At his home in Radicondoli, Tuscany, 1989

SHOOTING THE BEAR

Sir Michael Tippett

*Byzantine gold pendant
(4th–5th century AD)*

34

Anthony Burton *introduces this year's Prom premieres*

WHEN SIBELIUS IN HIS RETIREMENT was asked by visitors about his long-awaited (and in the end never completed) Eighth Symphony, he simply quoted a Scandinavian proverb: 'One doesn't sell the bearskin until one has shot the bear'. The saying came back to me more than once while I was talking to the composers of this season's new works. Because of the publication date of the Proms Guide, our conversations were taking place six months or more before their works were due to be performed. And so several of them were understandably reluctant to 'sell the bearskin' – to describe in detail their conception of pieces which they were still writing, and which might undergo radical changes in the course of composition.

Happily, though, the two senior figures among this season's batch of composers, Tippett and Lutoslawski, have maintained a remarkable fluency of output and inspiration (the opposite of Sibelius's silence in his retirement), and their bearskins are already on display – the scores completed and ready well in advance. Indeed, **Sir Michael Tippett**'s *Byzantium*, for soprano and large orchestra, will have had its first performances in Chicago and New York nearly five months before its European premiere in Prom 58. The solo part, written for Jessye Norman, will be sung in London by Faye Robinson, who will be familiar to Prom audiences through her memorable performances in Tippett's *A Child of Our Time* and *The Mask of Time*. The BBC Symphony Orchestra will be conducted by another leading Tippett specialist, Andrew Davis.

Tippett says of *Byzantium* that 'it's turned out a really big piece – I'm surprised, I can't quite make out how it came about – but at the same time much more delicate than I expected'. Unusually for him, since for most of his career he has written his own texts, it is a setting of a poem by W.B. Yeats. The poem's images, of the richness of the holy city of Byzantium and of the sea as viewed from Yeats's tower on the west coast of

Tippett sitting on W. B. Yeats's bed at Yeats's Tower, Thor Ballylee, County Galway, June 1988

Ireland, are conveyed in music which even on the page looks full of colour and light, as well as of Tippett's characteristic driving energy.

Witold Lutoslawski, who at seventy-eight is Tippett's junior by eight years, will be making one of his ever-welcome appearances with the BBC Symphony Orchestra in Prom 24, to conduct his Cello Concerto and the world premiere of his latest work, *Chantefleurs et Chantefables*. This too is for soprano and orchestra, but otherwise it could hardly be more different from Tippett's *Byzantium*: it is a set of miniatures accompanied by a chamber orchestra including harp, piano and percussion but only one of each wind instrument.

Lutoslawski prefers to set texts in 'international' languages, rather than in his native Polish; and here he has gone back to the work of the French poet Robert Desnos, who died in 1945 in the Terezin concentration camp. He set a rich, allusive poem by Desnos in his last vocal work, *Les Espaces du sommeil* for baritone and orchestra, in 1975. But this time he has chosen as his texts nine of a collection of Desnos's poems for children – beloved of successive generations of young French readers since its first full publication in 1955 – on subjects drawn from the natural world: flowers, insects, animals.

Lutoslawski himself says that these delightful poems 'inspired me to write very simple textures and for rather a small ensemble'. The result is 'something entirely different' both from his other works for voice and orchestra and from his early, utilitarian collections of chil-

dren's songs – and this time 'not exactly for children'. The solo part was written for the young Norwegian singer Solveig Kringlebotn, by whom Lutoslawski was 'absolutely enchanted' when he heard her in a recital in Warsaw; he describes her as a 'very light soprano with a beautiful colour of voice, with apparently effortless production, and theatrical without exaggeration'.

Pieces for voice and orchestra seem to be in vogue this year: Prom 3 will include the first performance of an orchestral song-cycle called *Some Days* by **Mark-Anthony Turnage**. Turnage had a spectacular success at last year's Proms with his ferocious *Three Screaming Popes*, in which Simon Rattle conducted the City of Birmingham Symphony Orchestra – the orchestra with which he is now Composer in Association. This work, though, was written in 1989, just before he took up the Birmingham post: it is one of the series of commissions by the David Cohen Charitable Trust for the Orchestra of the Royal Opera House. Turnage describes this as an 'amazing opportunity' to write for the conductor Bernard Haitink, whom he greatly admires, and for the Covent Garden orchestra, with its 'particularly good string section'.

This emphasis on the strings is important because, in contrast to *Three Screaming Popes*, the new work does not use the full orchestra, but is confined to strings together with clarinets, bassoons and harp. This reflects what Turnage describes as a greater emphasis on lyrical melodic lines in his recent music – though in common with many of his earlier works *Some Days* shows the influence of the jazz trumpeter Miles Davis, and its overall feeling is that of the blues. The piece is based on poems by black writers from Africa and America. So, although Turnage wrote the solo part without a specific singer in mind, he is delighted with the choice of the black American mezzo Cynthia Clarey – Hannah in last year's Prom performance of Tippett's *The Ice Break*.

Elements of popular music of different traditions also appear in new works by two contemporaries of Turnage (which is to say just entering their thirties), David Sawer and Martin Butler. **David Sawer** will be represented at

Mark-Anthony Turnage

Witold Lutoslawski

Robert Desnos (1900–45)

David Sawer

Wartime terminus

the Proms for the first time by the British premiere of his *Songs of Love and War*, in the late-evening Prom 23, given by the BBC Singers with their conductor Simon Joly. This work, for chorus with two percussionists and two harps, was commissioned by the BBC for a concert which the Singers gave during a visit to Frankfurt last December.

Sawer's title is a parody of the title of Monteverdi's Eighth Book of Madrigals, *Madrigali guerrieri ed amorosi*. And indeed the title, he says, 'was the first thing I had. I looked around for ages for poems'. A primary consideration was the need for a text which would allow him to treat the twenty-four members of the Singers as individual soloists, rather than writing 'a one-dimensional choir piece'. Finally he hit on the idea of using the words – though not the tunes – of a dozen popular songs of the Second World War, in a sequence which would suggest the emotions of war through the language of the songs.

Sawer says that the work is a result of his 'awful fascination with the whole business of war: the way it suddenly changes people's perceptions and behaviour'. His theatrical instincts – he has worked primarily as a composer and performer of music-theatre works – are satisfied by the stage layout of the piece, with the women spatially divided from the men, and by its narrative structure. The songs are used in the order in which they first came out, and they stop short in the middle of the war: so there is no happy ending, just an abiding image of separation.

River meandering through tropical rain forest, Ecuador

Martin Butler was first represented at the Proms in 1988 by a neatly turned ensemble piece called *Tin-Pan Ballet*. Now a BBC commission has enabled him to compose a much more ambitious new work, to be given its first performance by the BBC Symphony Orchestra under Matthias Bamert in Prom 28. Butler says that as he composed the work – it was finished last autumn – he found himself 'revelling in the idea of having an orchestra used to playing modern scores'.

An important element in the piece is provided by the rhythms and colours of Latin-American and Spanish dance music; there are also hints of some of the harmonic techniques of jazz arrangers. Butler declares himself fascinated by the idea of incorporating different stylistic elements in each of his works: 'I've tried very hard to get away from the idea of "finding my own voice". Exploring is the interesting part!'

The title of Butler's piece is *O Rio*: not an exclamation, but simply the Portuguese for 'the river'. He likens the overall shape of the piece to the course of a great river, flowing onwards with sometimes gradual and sometimes abrupt changes of surroundings. An underlying melody suggests the river's journey, and at the end of the piece this melodic line at last appears on its own in a sonorous unison.

But superimposed on this scheme are allusions to the northern Brazilian myth of the 'jakui' – powerful spirits which live in the river, and which take the form of flutes. The legend describes how one man cunningly catches one of these spirits in a net and learns to play it, thus harnessing so much creative power that even the sun and moon are jealous. These allusions are particularly clear in the central section of *O Rio*, in which three flutes play a prominent part, sometimes with an 'energetic shadow' of three trumpets.

As Butler outlines this legend, it begins to take on uncanny echoes of the way in which **Malcolm Williamson**, the Master of the Queen's Music, describes his new BBC commission, *Myth of the Cave*. This will have its premiere, in a slightly premature celebration of Williamson's sixtieth birthday in November, in Prom 12,

Martin Butler

THE ART
OF
ENCOURAGING
GOOD MUSIC

A SPECIAL KIND OF ANIMAL

*One in a series of illustrations by The Royal
College of Art Students, specially commissioned by Esso.*

Shadows on a cave wall: paintings of spirit figures known as 'Wandjinas', from the Dog cave area, Napier Range, Western Australia

Malcolm Williamson

Hugh Wood

played by James Galway with the BBC Concert Orchestra under Barry Wordsworth.

Williamson's primary source of inspiration is the allegory of the cave in Plato's *Republic*. This describes a group of prisoners confined in a cave in such a way that their sole knowledge of reality is through shadows cast on the cave wall. At length one man breaks free, and in the outside world painfully acquires a knowledge of reality which will ultimately enable him to become a leader of his fellows.

This classical Greek fable has fascinated Williamson for many years. He finds in it anticipations of Christian belief, and also connections with the aboriginal tribes of his own native Australia – cave-dwellers in ancient times, whose civilisation before it was destroyed had many of the features of Plato's ideal democracy.

Williamson's long-term aim is to write a three-act ballet based on the story of the cave. But in the meantime this plan has merged with another, to compose a flute concerto for James Galway. In the early 1960s, Galway played in the orchestra for Williamson's first opera, *Our Man in Havana*, and acquired a liking for his music; Williamson in turn describes Galway as 'a very fine artist: I'm honoured to be collaborating with him'. He has taken up two of Galway's suggestions: that the soloist should play not only the standard flute but also the piccolo and alto flute; and that the orchestral flutes should also have an important role.

In Williamson's overall plan, the Prom piece will eventually constitute the first act of the ballet score, taking the story as far as the protagonist's departure from the cave. The solo flute (an instrument central to Greek culture) will represent this central character, the 'philosopher-ruler' who painfully searches for knowledge. The music will be sectional but continuous; and it will include three choral songs, to poems by the contemporary writer Ruth Padel – a further ingredient in what already sounds like a rich mixture.

When I talked to Williamson he was still hard at work on his score. So too was his near-contemporary **Hugh Wood** when I asked him about his new Piano Concerto, a BBC commission for Prom 63. In fact, it was Wood who reminded me of Sibelius's proverb about the bearskin, and professed a dislike for any form of advance publicity while the piece was still in progress.

However, he was prepared to say that it will have a traditional three-movement outline, and its central slow movement will be a set of variations on an (unidentified) old song, with the theme – as in Britten's *Lachrymae* – 'gradually emerging from a fog' at the end of the movement. All of which sounds like a further demonstration of what Wood's fellow-composer Anthony Payne has called his 'determination to maintain freshness against the background of traditional techniques and modes of thought'.

If he is taciturn about the concerto, Wood talks with much greater enthusiasm about the pianist for whom he is writing it, Joanna MacGregor – who made an impressive Prom debut last summer in Ravel's Concerto for the left hand. She studied composition with Wood as a Cambridge undergraduate, and he was struck then by her enquiring mind, and 'absolutely astonished' by the quality of her playing. He is worried that he will be unable to write a solo part difficult enough to stretch her. But will the concerto reflect her personality, or at least her lively platform persona? 'I hope so, if you mean something brash and extrovert. I've done my level best.' And in turn Joanna MacGregor discerns Wood's

38

personality in what she has seen so far of the new work. 'It's terribly chunky and meaty and lyrical, like his violin and cello concertos – very gritty and very personal.'

Another substantial BBC commission which at the beginning of the year was still 'work in progress' is the Symphony by **Peter Paul Nash**, to be played by the BBC Symphony Orchestra under Peter Eötvös in Prom 50. Nash, forty last year, is well known to Radio 3 listeners as presenter of *Music Weekly* and other programmes, but this will be his first appearance at the Proms as a composer.

He says that, although his work is based on an extra-musical narrative, this is filtered through his emotional responses in such a way that it would be misleading to say what it was. However, he does vouchsafe that the piece grows out of his interest in catastrophe – 'the way people court it and even dally with it. The twin poles of the music are catastrophe and playfulness'.

The symphony, Nash says, is carefully pre-planned in every aspect: 'It's full of systems – I don't think there's an unexplained note in it'. But he is insistent that the right kind of system will produce rather than inhibit the organic growth of the material. He certainly does not think the results will sound unspontaneous, pointing to the enormous amount of calculation that is now known to have gone into the work even of such an apparently instinctive composer as Debussy. And he considers it important to give the orchestral players the kind of line which encourages them to take individual responsibility for musical expression: 'fully possessing the line and playing it for all it's worth'.

The season's two remaining BBC commissions were less far advanced than Nash's when I talked to their composers. **Nicholas Maw**, whose massive *Odyssey* began its life at the Proms in 1987, was concentrating on completing a piano trio for the Bath Festival; but he was already thinking about the sound-world, if not yet the details, of the next piece on his agenda, *American Games*. This will be played by the North Western University Wind Ensemble from Illinois, with its conductor John P. Paynter, in the late-night Prom 6.

Maw says that, although he has spent most of his time in the United States in the last few years, until now none of the music he has written there has been 'consciously American'. Now he wants to write a piece which reflects its predominantly American medium: 'Playing in a band is an activity carried on by young people, like games. It's associated with health and vigour'. At the same time he suspects that the kind of outdoor, community life which he wants to celebrate may already be disappearing, and the piece 'may touch on my thoughts about that'.

Meanwhile **Martin Dalby** was contemplating the work he will be writing for the Royal Scottish National Orchestra to play under Sir Alexander Gibson in Prom 34. Dalby has recently stepped down as the BBC's Head of Music in Scotland after eighteen years, to return to a production role – a move which is intended to leave him more time for composing. He has already begun making 'random sketches, to get my writing going again', but these have not yet crystallised into an overall shape.

Dalby does, however, have an animating idea for the piece, represented in its title *The Mary Bean*. This, he explains, is a bean which grows in the Caribbean: 'It propagates itself by dropping into the sea, and getting washed away to somewhere else. Sometimes beans get carried away in the Gulf Stream, and deposited on the western shores of Scotland, or in the Western Isles. And since they're not indigenous, the local people collect them and wear them as good-luck charms.' Dalby thinks this story will lead on to ideas about other arrivals in Scotland, including St Columba – to be represented by some little-known fragments of Celtic chant. And he hopes *The Mary Bean* will also act as a good-luck charm for the Royal Scottish National orchestra itself.

But for Dalby, as for some of his colleagues, the business of putting the notes on paper, the composer's eternal bear-hunt, is still in progress. Only when the conductor's baton comes down will we know what the bearskin is really like.

Peter Paul Nash

Nicholas Maw

Martin Dalby

PROMS 91 ARTISTS

Semyon Bychkov

RICHARD HOLT

Simon Rattle

EMI/VICTORIA MIHICH

Claudio Abbado

CLIVE BARDA

Vladimir Ashkenazy

GODFREY MACDOMNIC

Jukka-Pekka Saraste

KATIE VANDYCK

Franz Welser-Möst

EMI/CHRIS GARNHAM

Klaus Tennstedt

GODFREY MACDOMNIC

Sir Charles Mackerras

ZOË DOMINIC

Gennady Rozhdestvensky

Seiji Ozawa

GODFREY MACDOMNIC

Richard Hickox

Ronald Corp

DICK SCOTT-STEWART

HANYA CHLALA

Michael Tilson Thomas

MALCOLM CROWTHERS

Mark Elder

David Atherton

ZOË DOMINIC

CLIVE BARDA

Andrew Litton

SUZIE E. MAEDER

40

Bernard Haitink

Jerzy Maksymiuk

Andrew Parrott

Mark Wigglesworth

Jane Glover

Yan Pascal Tortelier

Tadaaki Otaka

Alexander Gibson   Barry Wordsworth

Alexander Lazarev

Sir Colin Davis

Figures refer to Prom numbers
*First appearance at a Henry
Wood Promenade Concert

CONDUCTORS

HANYA CHLALA

Maria Ewing

ZOË DOMINIC

Felicity Lott

Willard White

HANYA CHLALA

CLIVE BARDA

Sergey Leiferkus

Solveig Kringlebotn

CLIVE BARDA

Kathleen Kuhlmann

ZOË DOMINIC

Mary King

HANYA CHLALA

Emily Van Evera

BENTE BJERCKE

Anthony Rolfe Johnson

EMI/STEVE HICKEY

James Bowman

CLIVE BARDA

Judith Howarth

Suzanne Murphy

Ann Murray

HANYA CHLALA

Evelyn Tubb

ALEX VON KOETTLITZ

David Wilson-Johnson

John Mark Ainsley

Linda Finnie

Philip Langridge

Figures refer to Prom numbers

*First appearance at a Henry
Wood Promenade Concert

Karita Mattila

Dame Gwyneth Jones

Cheryl Studer

John Tomlinson

Diana Montague

Dennis O'Neill

Ann Howard **41**
Judith Howarth* **33**
Anthony Rolfe Johnson **51**
Dame Gwyneth Jones **67**
Simon Keenlyside* **35**
Andrew King **4**
Mary King **39**
Solveig Kringlebotn* **24**
David Kuebler* **33**
Kathleen Kuhlmann **51**
Gary Lakes* **15**
Philip Langridge **44**
Sergey Leiferkus* **41**
Keith Lewis **1**
Felicity Lott **47**
Martine Mahe* **44**
Karita Mattila **25**
Donald Maxwell **41**
Peter Mikulas* **33**
Alistair Miles **20**
Diana Montague **44**
Suzanne Murphy **66**
Ann Murray **64**
Dennis O'Neill **66**
Felicity Palmer **41**
Ashley Putnam* **44**
Florence Quivar **1**
Jean Rigby **28**
Catherine Robbin **20**
Faye Robinson **58**
Anthony Roden **66**
Joan Rodgers **27**
Nigel Rogers **4**
Gianna Rolandi **19**
Amanda Roocroft* **66**
Peter Rose **44**
Cheryl Studer* **46**
Elzbieta Szmytka* **44**
Robert Tear **41**
John Tomlinson **48, 51**
Evelyn Tubb **4**
Emily Van Evera **4**
Penelope Walmsley-Clark **60**
Lilian Watson **48**
Willard White **1**
David Wilson-Johnson **27**

John Mark Ainsley **20, 66**
David Maxwell Anderson* **41**
Nancy Argenta **20**
Brian Bannatyne-Scott* **41**
James Bowman **35**
Ian Caley **50**
Michael Chance **27**
Cynthia Clarey **3**
Joseph Cornwell **4**
Rogers Covey-Crump **35**
Laurence Dale **19**
Charles Daniels* **35**
Maldwyn Davies **27**
Jane Eaglen **51**
Francis Egerton **41**
Maria Ewing **13**
Linda Finnie **15**
Gillian Fisher **35**
Michael George **35**
Galina Gorchakova* **41**
Håkan Hagegård **19**
Alfreda Hodgson **19**

43

Sabine Meyer

Barry Tuckwell

Kevin Bowyer

Andrea Lucchesini

Moura Lympany

Alfred Brendel

Emanuel Ax

Yuri Bashmet

Peter Donohoe

James Galway

Piers Lane

Sidonie Goossens

Joshua Bell

Stephen Hough

Dmitry Sitkovetsky

Tasmin Little

Dong-Suk Kang

Dmitri Alexeev* **11**
Emanuel Ax **37**
Yuri Bashmet **18**
Joshua Bell **45**
William Bennett **64**
Philippe Bianconi* **52**
Neil Black **64**
Nigel Boddice* **32**
Tom Bowes* **27**
Kevin Bowyer* **36**
Julian Bream **2**
Alfred Brendel **46**
Iona Brown **14**
Robert Cohen **21**
Paul Crossley **13**
Peter Donohoe **17**
James Galway **12**
Sidonie Goossens **67**
Natalia Gutman **24**
Stephen Hough **15**
Jeffrey Kahane* **7**
Christopher van Kampen **13**
Dong-Suk Kang **16**
Ralph Kirshbaum **29**
Gidon Kremer* **56**
Piers Lane **2**
John Lill **30**
Tasmin Little **22**
Frank Lloyd **64**
Andrea Lucchesini* **5**
Moura Lympany **34**
Joanna MacGregor **63**
Sabine Meyer* **8**
Olli Mustonen* **26**
Celia Nicklin **27**
Kurt Nikkanen* **49**
Robin O'Neill* **64**
David Owen Norris **32**
Miklós Perényi* **38**
Artur Pizarro* **54**
Dmitry Sitkovetsky **42**
Kathryn Stott **48**
Michael Thompson **50**
Barry Tuckwell **9**
Mitsuko Uchida **64**

Julian Bream

Gidon Kremer

Mitsuko Uchida

Olli Mustonen

Robert Cohen

Natalia Gutman

Christopher van Kampen

Kathryn Stott

Kurt Nikkanen

Joanna MacGregor

Artur Pizarro

PROMS 91 ARTISTS

The King's Consort

Iona Brown

Taverner Consort

BBC Symphony Chorus

Dame Judi Dench

Roy Goodman

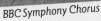

BBC Singers

ORCHESTRAS

BBC Concert Orchestra **2, 12**
BBC Philharmonic **8, 9, 41, 42**
BBC Scottish Symphony
  Orchestra **21, 22, 32**
BBC Symphony Orchestra
  **1, 5, 11, 15, 19, 24, 28, 33, 39,
  45, 50, 54, 58, 63, 67**
BBC Welsh Symphony
  Orchestra **16, 17, 48**
Berlin Philharmonic Orchestra*
  46
Boston Symphony Orchestra **59**
Bournemouth Symphony
  Orchestra **7**
City of Birmingham Symphony
  Orchestra **56, 57**
Dresden Staatskapelle* **61, 62**
English Chamber Orchestra **64**
European Community Youth
  Orchestra **43**
Finnish Radio Symphony
  Orchestra* **25, 26**
Gustav Mahler Jugendorchester*
  38
London Classical Players **20**
London Mozart Players **27**
The London Philharmonic
  44, 47, 51
London Sinfonietta **13**
London Symphony Orchestra **65**
National Youth Orchestra
  of Great Britain **18**
New London Orchestra* **60**
Norwegian Chamber Orchestra*
  14
Orchestra of the Royal Opera
  House, Covent Garden **3**
Orchestra of Welsh National
  Opera **66**
Orchestre de Paris **52, 53**
Orpheus Chamber Orchestra*
  40
The Philharmonia **37**
Royal Liverpool Philharmonic
  Orchestra **29, 30**
Royal Philharmonic Orchestra
  49
Royal Scottish National
  Orchestra **34**

MISCELLANEOUS

Iona Brown* **14**
Dame Judi Dench* **60**
Roy Goodman* **10**
Robert King* **35**
James O'Donnell* **55**

ENSEMBLES

Brandenburg Consort* **10**
Capricorn* **23**
Finchley Children's Music Group
  60
The King's Consort* **35**
London Gabrieli Brass
  Ensemble* **51**
Northwestern University
  Symphonic Wind Ensemble* **6**
Taverner Consort and Players **4**

CHOIRS

BBC Singers
  1, 5, 12, 19, 23, 27, 41, 67
BBC Symphony Chorus
  1, 19, 28, 33, 58, 67
The Choir of the
  King's Consort* **35**
Chorus of Welsh National
  Opera **66**
Glyndebourne Chorus **44**
London Philharmonic Choir **1, 51**
London Symphony Chorus
  48, 65
New London Chamber Choir* **4**
Philharmonia Chorus **28**
Schütz Choir of London **20**
Taverner Choir **4**
USSR Ministry of Culture
  Chamber Choir* **31, 33**
Westminster Cathedral Choir **55**

47

PROGRAMMES 91

INFORMATION

Full details of this year's Prom programmes are given in the following pages, together with booking instructions and a booking form. Although every effort will be made to adhere to the programmes as advertised, the BBC reserves the right to make any necessary changes.

Doors open three quarters of an hour before each concert; on days when there are two concerts in the Royal Albert Hall, there may be a slight delay in the opening of doors for the second concert.

Broadcasting

All concerts will be broadcast in stereo on BBC Radio 3, and some will be shown on BBC television. For details see *Radio Times* each week. In view of these broadcasts, we ask all patrons attending Proms to bear in mind the need for **absolute silence** during the performance of the music. Please show your consideration for the musicians, your neighbours in the audience, and those listening to the broadcast by **not coughing** during the music, and by **turning off alarms** on watches and calculators before the concert begins.

Latecomers

Latecomers will not be admitted to the auditorium unless or until there is a suitable break in the music.

Access to Promenade areas

Unaccompanied blind patrons who wish to be admitted to the Arena or Gallery are asked to contact the Hall Manager in advance.

Reminders

The management of the Royal Albert Hall reminds concert-goers that they **must not smoke, take photographs, or make recordings** in the auditorium. Coats and hats only may be left in the cloakrooms. Hand-luggage larger than a briefcase, food and drink, and folding chairs will not be allowed into the Hall. Children under the age of five years are not permitted in the Hall. Tickets shall not be sold or offered for sale in the vicinity of the Royal Albert Hall. The management reserves the right to refuse admission.

Stewards

Royal Albert Hall stewards directing queues outside the Hall have no authority or responsibility other than to guide patrons.

Programmes for Promenaders

Promenaders may buy programmes at a reduced price in the Arena and Gallery only.

PRE-PROM TALKS

Informal half-hour talks about aspects of the evening's music will precede a number of concerts. The first two talks of the season, on July 21 and 26, will be given in the Imperial College Students Union, Prince Consort Road (entrance in Bremner Road, south-west of the Albert Hall). All other talks will be held in the Concert Hall of the Royal College of Music, Prince Consort Road (immediately south of the Albert Hall). The ELLSO Workshop (29 July) will be in the Recital Hall of the Royal College of Music. Admission is free, but because of limited accommodation cannot be guaranteed. All talks will begin at 6.15pm, except 26 July (5.45pm) and 29 July (6.30pm), and there will be no admittance from 5 minutes after the start.

Mark-Anthony Turnage	21 July 6.15pm
Robin Holloway	26 July 5.45pm
Malcolm Williamson	28 July 6.15pm
ELLSO Workshop	29 July 6.30pm
Witold Lutoslawski	8 August 6.15pm
Martin Butler	12 August 6.15pm
Martin Dalby	17 August 6.15pm
Peter Paul Nash	30 August 6.15pm
Sir Michael Tippett	6 September 6.15pm
Hugh Wood	10 September 6.15pm

FRIDAY 19 JULY

7.30pm *ending at approximately 9.40pm*

Elgar
The Dream of Gerontius

Part 1   36

INTERVAL

Part 2   61

Florence Quivar *mezzo-soprano*
Keith Lewis *tenor*
Willard White *bass*

BBC Singers
BBC Symphony Chorus
London Philharmonic Choir
BBC Symphony Orchestra
Andrew Davis *conductor*

To the delight of all lovers of English music, the 1991 Prom season opens with a 'Best of British' weekend. Andrew Davis recently won a Royal Philharmonic Society Charles Heidsieck Award for 'leading the BBC Symphony Orchestra through an outstanding Diamond Jubilee season'. He possesses a notable reputation as an Elgar interpreter, and here conducts a distinguished line-up of soloists with BBC forces in Elgar's choral masterpiece – the first of several original commissions for the Birmingham Festival featured this season. Cardinal Newman's famous metaphysical poem describes the pilgrimage of a newly-liberated soul to the awesome Judgement Seat, and thence to Purgatory, to await the 'truth of everlasting day'.

Commentary by Wendy Thompson

SATURDAY 20 JULY

7.30pm *ending at approximately 9.40pm*

Walton
Crown Imperial   7

Bliss
Piano Concerto   37

INTERVAL

Malcolm Arnold
Guitar Concerto   21

Vaughan Williams
Symphony No. 8 in D minor   27

Piers Lane *piano*

Julian Bream *guitar*

BBC Concert Orchestra
Barry Wordsworth *conductor*

A celebration of two birthdays: Bliss's centenary, and Malcolm Arnold's seventieth. Australian pianist Piers Lane – a frequent broadcaster on Radio 3 – tackles Bliss's unashamedly Romantic Piano Concerto, while the leading British guitarist Julian Bream (who in January this year gave his fortieth-anniversary concert at the Wigmore Hall) plays Arnold's Guitar Concerto, specially written for him, and premiered at the 1953 Aldeburgh Festival. The BBC Concert Orchestra under Barry Wordsworth has recently completed a series of recordings of works by British composers.

SUNDAY 21 JULY

7.30pm *ending at approximately 9.30pm*

Pre-Prom talk at 6.15pm
Mark-Anthony Turnage

Britten
Four Sea-Interludes from 'Peter Grimes'   16

Mark-Anthony Turnage
Some Days
world premiere   15

INTERVAL

Elgar
Symphony No. 1 in A flat major   52

Cynthia Clarey *mezzo-soprano*

Orchestra of the Royal Opera House,
  Covent Garden
Bernard Haitink *conductor*

Britten's evocative *Sea-Interludes* and Elgar's noble First Symphony frame a world premiere by Mark-Anthony Turnage, whose startlingly original opera *Greek* caused a sensation on its London production last year. The American mezzo-soprano Cynthia Clarey – widely acclaimed for her Glyndebourne performances as Monteverdi's Ottavia and as Serena in *Porgy and Bess* – returns to the Proms as soloist in *Some Days* (see page 34). Bernard Haitink, Music Director of the Royal Opera since 1987, and initiator of the Garden Concerts (for which *Some Days* was commissioned) conducts the Covent Garden orchestra.

MONDAY 22 JULY

7.30pm *ending at approximately 9.25pm*

4

Monteverdi
Vespers 105

Evelyn Tubb *soprano*
Emily Van Evera *soprano*
Joseph Cornwell *tenor*
Andrew King *tenor*
Nigel Rogers *tenor*

New London Chamber Choir
Taverner Choir, Consort and Players
Andrew Parrott *conductor*

Andrew Parrott directs the Taverner Consort and Players in a reconsidered version of Monteverdi's magnificent *Vespers* of 1610, probably written for the Gonzaga ducal chapel of Santa Barbara in Mantua. This edition presents the *Vespers* not as a mere concert piece, but as a brilliant embellishment of the liturgy and its chant, with the music appropriately ordered and supplemented. One Psalm and the *Magnificat* are restored to their intended relative pitch, and solo voices are used almost throughout.

NB There will be no interval in this performance

TUESDAY 23 JULY

7.00pm *ending at approximately 8.50pm*

5

Luciano Berio
Coro 53

INTERVAL

Luciano Berio
Concerto II 'Echoing Curves' 25

Andrea Lucchesini *piano*

BBC Singers
BBC Symphony Orchestra
Luciano Berio *conductor*

Both works in this programme were performed as part of the BBC's highly successful Berio Festival, held in January last year at the Barbican. *Coro*, originally written for Cologne's West German Radio during 1975–6, is a setting, for 40 'pairs' of solo voices and instruments, of a series of folk texts interwoven with fragments from Pablo Neruda's trilogy *Residencia en la Tierra*, particularly those denouncing the atrocities of the Spanish Civil War. The young Italian pianist Andrea Lucchesini, winner of the 1983 Dino Ciani Competition, makes his Prom debut in *Echoing Curves* (1988–9). David Osmond-Smith introduces both works on page 32.

TUESDAY 23 JULY

10.00pm *ending at approximately 11.20pm*

6

Holst
Hammersmith 14
David Bedford
Sun Paints Rainbows on the Vast Waves 12
Nicholas Maw
American Games
BBC commission: world premiere 20
Skalkottas
Greek Dances – selection 20

Northwestern University Symphonic Wind
  Ensemble
John P. Paynter *conductor*

John P. Paynter, one of America's leading band conductors, has been Director of Bands at Northwestern University, Illinois, since 1953. In his second year he founded the university's renowned Symphonic Wind Ensemble, now achieving international recognition. David Bedford's *Sun Paints Rainbows on the Vast Waves*, inspired by a jotting in the poet Coleridge's notebook, was commissioned by the 1982 Huddersfield Festival. It requires a 'massive sound', according to Bedford. Anthony Burton writes on Nicholas Maw's new piece on page 34.

SPECIAL OFFER!

WEDNESDAY 24 JULY

7.30pm *ending at approximately 9.30pm*

Gershwin
Cuban Overture 10

Bernstein
Symphony No. 2 'The Age of Anxiety' 30

INTERVAL

Sibelius
Symphony No. 2 in D major 43

Jeffrey Kahane *piano*

Bournemouth Symphony Orchestra
Andrew Litton *conductor*

American pianist Jeffrey Kahane joins his dynamic compatriot Andrew Litton, the BSO's Principal Conductor since 1988, in this programme with a strong transatlantic flavour. The great American composer, conductor and communicator Leonard Bernstein is commemorated with a performance of his Second Symphony, inspired by W.H. Auden's 'fascinating and hair-raising poem' *The Age of Anxiety* and written in 1949. Scored for piano and orchestra, the work records 'our difficult and problematical search for faith', the pianist, Bernstein said, representing 'an almost autobiographical protagonist, set against an orchestral mirror in which he sees himself analytically, in the modern ambience'.

THURSDAY 25 JULY

7.30pm *ending at approximately 9.30pm*

Mozart
Clarinet Concerto in A major, K622 29

INTERVAL

Bruckner
Symphony No. 9 in D minor 55

Sabine Meyer *clarinet*

BBC Philharmonic
Bernhard Klee *conductor*

Bernhard Klee, former Chief Guest Conductor of the BBC Philharmonic and currently Music Director of the North German Radio Orchestra in Hanover, has chosen two works of an elegiac nature to open the Philharmonic's Prom appearances this season. The brilliant young German virtuoso Sabine Meyer, whose controversial appointment to the Berlin Philharmonic Orchestra under Karajan caused a blaze of publicity, plays Mozart's reflective Clarinet Concerto. Completed less than three months before his death, it was to be his last orchestral work. Unlike Mozart, Bruckner realised that his Ninth Symphony (left unfinished at his death) would be his musical testament: he saw its moving Adagio as his own 'farewell to life'.

FRIDAY 26 JULY

7.00pm *ending at approximately 9.00pm*

Pre-Prom talk at 5.45pm
Robin Holloway

Elgar
In the South 20

Robin Holloway
Horn Concerto 29

INTERVAL

Dvořák
Symphony No. 8 in G major 37

Barry Tuckwell *horn*

BBC Philharmonic
Edward Downes *conductor*

This year Barry Tuckwell, the world's most recorded horn player, includes in his intensive worldwide performing, conducting and recording schedule a series of special sixtieth-birthday concerts at Carnegie Hall, the Royal Festival Hall, the Barbican and the Proms. Robin Holloway's Horn Concerto (1979–80) is one of many works by eminent contemporary composers inspired by Tuckwell's mellow tone and flexible technique. Although full of the idioms of his native Bohemia, Dvořák's lyrical, relaxed Eighth Symphony has been appropriated as the 'English'. The composer conducted performances of it in London and Cambridge, and it was first published here in 1892.

FRIDAY 26 JULY

10.00pm *ending at approximately 11.15pm*

Bach
Brandenburg Concerto No. 1 in F major,
BWV 1046   23
Corelli
Concerto Grosso in D major,
Op. 6 No. 4   20
Bach
Suite No. 4 in D major, BWV 1069   22

Brandenburg Consort
Roy Goodman *director*

Roy Goodman, Principal Conductor of the Hanover Band and Musical Director of the European Community Baroque Orchestra, re-formed the Brandenburg Consort last year with the intention of recording the wealth of Baroque repertoire by Bach and his contemporaries, especially Handel and Corelli. Their recording of the Bach orchestral Suites was released in May, to be followed by the Brandenburg Concertos. For this programme, marking the newly-resurrected ensemble's Prom debut, Goodman has chosen three contrasting examples of Baroque concerto form, each a model of its kind.

SATURDAY 27 JULY

7.30pm *ending at approximately 9.40pm*

Rimsky-Korsakov
Sheherazade   45
INTERVAL
Prokofiev
Piano Concerto No. 2 in G minor   33
Tchaikovsky
Overture '1812'   15

Dmitri Alexeev *piano*

BBC Symphony Orchestra
Alexander Lazarev *conductor*

Alexander Lazarev, Chief Conductor of the Bolshoy Theatre in Moscow, has worked on a number of occasions with the BBC Symphony Orchestra, most recently in the BBC's Henze Festival at the Barbican earlier this year. Russian pianist Dmitri Alexeev, winner of the 1975 Leeds International Piano Competition, is the soloist in Prokofiev's sardonic Second Piano Concerto, a work which provoked a near riot at its first performance in 1913. Tchaikovsky's '1812' Overture commemorates the historic retreat of Napoleon's army from Moscow. Characteristically, the self-critical composer himself didn't think much of it. 'It will be very loud and noisy', he wrote to his patron.

SUNDAY 28 JULY

7.30pm *ending at approximately 9.35pm*

Pre-Prom talk at 6.15pm
Malcolm Williamson

Schubert
Incidental music to 'Rosamunde'
– selection   15
Malcolm Williamson
Myth of the Cave – for flutes, chorus
and orchestra
BBC commission: world premiere   30
INTERVAL
Tchaikovsky
The Sleeping Beauty: Act 3   50

James Galway *flute, piccolo and alto flute*

BBC Singers
BBC Concert Orchestra
Barry Wordsworth *conductor*

Anthony Burton introduces the new work by Master of the Queen's Music Malcolm Williamson (who celebrates his sixtieth birthday this year) on page 34. The premiere of this quasi-concerto for one flautist with three flutes marks the welcome return to the Proms of the work's dedicatee, the versatile James Galway. The third act of Tchaikovsky's magical *Sleeping Beauty* contains the glittering sequence of tableaux which accompanies the wedding celebrations of Aurora and her Prince.

MONDAY 29 JULY

7.30pm *ending at approximately 9.40*

Pre-Prom workshop performance at 6.30pm

Webern
Five Pieces for Orchestra, Op. 10   6

Mahler arr. Schoenberg
Lieder eines fahrenden Gesellen   14

H.K. Gruber
Cello Concerto   20

INTERVAL

York Höller
Improvisation sur le nom de Pierre Boulez   4

Mahler arr. Reinbert de Leeuw
Kindertotenlieder   24

Alfred Schnittke
Concerto for Piano and Strings   22

Maria Ewing *soprano*
Christopher van Kampen *cello*
Paul Crossley *piano*

London Sinfonietta
Lothar Zagrosek *conductor*

H.K. Gruber's *Frankenstein!!* has enjoyed remarkable success. His recent Cello Concerto (1989) tempers Viennese *douceur* with undercurrents of cabaret culture. York Höller's brief homage to Boulez (1984–5) was composed just before his opera *The Master and Margarita*, premiered in 1989. Alfred Schnittke's one-movement concerto dates from 1979. The results of a composition project led by Nigel Osborne and London Sinfonietta players with the East London Late Starters Orchestra will be revealed at 6.30pm.

◀SPECIAL OFFER!▶

TUESDAY 30 JULY

7.30pm *ending at approximately 9.50pm*

Britten
Variations on a Theme of Frank Bridge   26

Strauss
Metamorphosen   27

INTERVAL

Mozart
Serenade in D major, K250 'Haffner'   50

Norwegian Chamber Orchestra
Iona Brown *violin/director*

Two major twentieth-century works for string orchestra open this programme by the Norwegian Chamber Orchestra, making its Prom debut under the direction of violinist Iona Brown. Strauss's eloquent 'study for 23 solo strings' was first conceived as a threnody for the wartime destruction of German cultural monuments, in particular the loss of his beloved National Theatre in Munich. In its final form it took on a deeper spiritual significance – a triumphant affirmation of creativity in the face of adversity, and an act of expiation for all guilt, destruction and suffering. In complete contrast is Mozart's light-hearted serenade, written for a friend's wedding celebration and enclosing a delicious miniature violin concerto.

WEDNESDAY 31 JULY

7.30pm *ending at approximately 9.35pm*

Mozart
Piano Concerto No. 9 in E flat major, K271   32

INTERVAL

Mahler
Das Lied von der Erde   63

Stephen Hough *piano*

Linda Finnie *mezzo-soprano*
Gary Lakes *tenor*

BBC Symphony Orchestra
Mark Elder *conductor*

A regular visitor to the Proms, Stephen Hough has recorded Brahms's Second Piano Concerto with the BBC Symphony Orchestra, and recently appeared on television with the BBC Scottish Symphony Orchestra in Mozart's K271. This concerto marked the composer's physical and artistic coming-of-age and broke new ground in exploring the relationship between soloist and orchestra while at the same time plumbing new depths of emotional maturity. Mahler's exquisite setting of Chinese poems, written under the shadow of a fatal illness, was in effect his 'Ninth Symphony', though according to his widow he did not 'venture to call it a symphony, owing to his superstition. And thus he thought to give God the slip ...'

THURSDAY 1 AUGUST

7.30pm *ending at approximately 9.35pm*

Grace Williams
Sea Sketches   18

Tchaikovsky
Violin Concerto in D major   35

INTERVAL

Prokofiev
Romeo and Juliet – excerpts   35

Dong-Suk Kang *violin*

BBC Welsh Symphony Orchestra
Tadaaki Otaka *conductor*

Hailed as one of the world's finest violinists,
Dong-Suk Kang made his Prom debut in the
Glazunov concerto in 1987, returning last year in
a televised performance of the Sibelius. He has
already appeared on television playing the Tchaikovsky with the BBC Welsh Symphony Orchestra. Grace Williams (1906–77) was a pupil of
Vaughan Williams and Egon Wellesz. She completed her *Sea Sketches* in bomb-scarred London
in 1944, and this five-movement suite vividly
reflects her nostalgic longing for the seascapes of
her native South Wales.

FRIDAY 2 AUGUST

7.30pm *ending at approximately 9.30pm*

Mozart
Symphony No. 32 in G major, K318
(Overture in the Italian style)   9

Sir Michael Tippett
Piano Concerto   34

INTERVAL

Strauss
Ein Heldenleben   40

Peter Donohoe *piano*

BBC Welsh Symphony Orchestra
Tadaaki Otaka *conductor*

Since his success in the 1983 Tchaikovsky Competition, Peter Donohoe's career has flourished.
One of the most energetic and combative British
pianists of his generation, he 'thirsts for new repertoire', and has consistently championed contemporary music. This year marks his thirteenth
consecutive Prom season. Strauss's last tone
poem, *Ein Heldenleben*, portrays 'a free ideal of
great and manly heroism'. Strauss called it his
'Eroica'. 'True', he admitted, 'it has no funeral
march, but it is in E flat major and has lots of
horns, which are, of course, well versed in
heroism ...'

SATURDAY 3 AUGUST

7.30pm *ending at approximately 9.45pm*

Walton
Viola Concerto   25

INTERVAL

Shostakovich
Symphony No. 7 in C major 'Leningrad'   73

Yuri Bashmet *viola*

National Youth Orchestra of Great Britain
David Atherton *conductor*

In a typically ambitious programme, the National
Youth Orchestra couples Walton's poetic Viola
Concerto, played by one of the outstanding Russian artists of our time, with Shostakovich's
courageous response to the Nazi siege of Leningrad in 1941. 'Working on the symphony, I
thought about the heroism of our nation, about
mankind's greatest ideals, about humanism and
beauty. In the name of all this we are fighting this
cruel war ...'

SUNDAY 4 AUGUST

7.30pm *ending at approximately 10.00pm*

Mendelssohn
Elijah

Part I   65

INTERVAL

Part 2   65

Gianna Rolandi *soprano*
Alfreda Hodgson *contralto*
Laurence Dale *tenor*
Håkan Hagegård *baritone*

BBC Singers
BBC Symphony Chorus
BBC Symphony Orchestra
Andrew Davis *conductor*

One of the monuments of the oratorio tradition, *Elijah* was commissioned for the 1846 Birmingham Festival. Mendelssohn himself seems to have done most of the work on the German text, but was also closely involved in the preparation of the English translation, and the piece has always enjoyed greater popularity in its English version (which will be sung at the Proms). The premiere, conducted by the composer, was a tremendous success: Mendelssohn clearly succeeded in his stated aim — 'to bring this magnificent text home to the hearts of my hearers'.

MONDAY 5 AUGUST

7.30pm *ending at approximately 9.25pm*

Mozart
Symphony No. 38 in D major, K504
'Prague'   29

INTERVAL

Mozart
Requiem   54

Nancy Argenta *soprano*
Catherine Robbin *contralto*
John Mark Ainsley *tenor*
Alistair Miles *bass*

Schütz Choir of London
London Classical Players
Roger Norrington *conductor*

It's Mozart all the way this year, and in the first of the season's Proms to be devoted entirely to the work of Salzburg's most famous son, Roger Norrington and the London Classical Players — who last year brought their *Magic Flute* to the Albert Hall — turn their expert restoration techniques to the 'Prague' Symphony and the *Requiem*, once again stripping away the accretions of two centuries to reveal the patina of a master craftsman.

TUESDAY 6 AUGUST

7.30pm *ending at approximately 9.40pm*

Sibelius
En Saga   19
Britten
Symphony for Cello and Orchestra   37

INTERVAL

Beethoven
Symphony No. 7 in A major   38

Robert Cohen *cello*

BBC Scottish Symphony Orchestra
Jerzy Maksymiuk *conductor*

Beethoven was not Britten's favourite composer. He found the German master's more rumbustious, unbuttoned moods particularly disconcerting, and this programme contrasts both composers at perhaps their most extreme — Britten introverted and idiosyncratic; Beethoven in full swing. Now enjoying a worldwide solo, ensemble and recital career, Robert Cohen made his first recording — of the Elgar concerto — aged only nineteen, and recently released all the Bach Solo Suites on disc. The BBC Scottish Symphony Orchestra makes the first of its annual Prom appearances under its flamboyant Chief Conductor, Jerzy Maksymiuk.

WEDNESDAY 7 AUGUST

7.00pm *ending at approximately 8.55pm*

Iannis Xenakis
Shaar   13

Dvořák
Violin Concerto in A minor   32

INTERVAL

Stravinsky
Petrushka (1947)   34

Tasmin Little *violin*

BBC Scottish Symphony Orchestra
Jerzy Maksymiuk *conductor*

Following her acclaimed Prom debut last year in the Janáček Concerto, Tasmin Little returns with a better-known product of Czech nationalism by the composer whom Janáček most revered. Iannis Xenakis has enjoyed a long and close association with the BBC Scottish Symphony Orchestra and Jerzy Maksymiuk. *Shaar*, commissioned by the Jerusalem Contemporary Music Festival in 1983, was given its UK premiere in a special Xenakis festival mounted four years ago by the BBC SSO in Glasgow. The title means 'Gate', and the work depicts a demonic struggle between the forces of good and evil.

WEDNESDAY 7 AUGUST

10.00pm *ending at approximately 11.15pm*

David Sawer
Songs of Love and War
BBC commission: UK premiere   13

Steve Reich
The Desert Music   48

BBC Singers
Capricorn
Simon Joly *conductor*

Last year's concert of *a cappella* music by Brahms, Strauss and Schoenberg given by the BBC Singers under Simon Joly was enjoyed by a full Albert Hall. This season they return with Steve Reich's *The Desert Music* (1982–3), a setting of poems by William Carlos Williams for eight-part chorus and orchestra, premiered here in the 1985 Proms. The text conjures up an uncompromising view of existence in the nuclear age: 'Man has survived hitherto because he was too ignorant to know how to realise his wishes. Now that he can realise them, he must either change or perish'. Anthony Burton writes about David Sawer's *Songs of Love and War* on page 34.

SPECIAL OFFER!

THURSDAY 8 AUGUST

7.30pm *ending at approximately 9.30pm*

Pre-Prom talk at 6.15pm
Witold Lutoslawski

Britten
Sinfonia da Requiem   20

Witold Lutoslawski
Chantefleurs et Chantefables *
world premiere   15

INTERVAL

Witold Lutoslawski
Cello Concerto *   23

Bartók
Music for Strings, Percussion and Celesta
                                                                        26

Solveig Kringlebotn *soprano*

Natalia Gutman *cello*

BBC Symphony Orchestra
Witold Lutoslawski *conductor* *
Mark Wigglesworth *conductor*

Witold Lutoslawski conducts two of his own works within a framework of twentieth-century masterworks by two of the composers he most admires. His dramatic Cello Concerto, premiered by Rostropovich in London in 1970, incorporates microtones and aleatory techniques, yet has proved one of his most accessible pieces (see page 34 for details of his new work). Winner of the 1989 International Kondrashin Competition and one of Britain's brightest young conductors, Mark Wigglesworth conducted the BBC Symphony Orchestra at the Barbican earlier this year, and here makes his Prom debut.

SPECIAL OFFER!

FRIDAY 9 AUGUST

7.30pm *ending at approximately 9.30pm*

Schumann
Overture, Scherzo and Finale   17

Magnus Lindberg
Kinetics
UK premiere   14

INTERVAL

Sibelius
Pohjola's Daughter   13

Höstkväll   6

Luonnotar   9

Mahler
Adagio from Symphony No. 10   23

Karita Mattila *soprano*

Finnish Radio Symphony Orchestra
Jukka-Pekka Saraste *conductor*

The young Finnish composer Magnus Lindberg (born in 1958) studied with Franco Donatoni and Gérard Grisey, and his intense and dramatic music has won him several prizes. *Kinetics* (1988–9), his fourth piece for large orchestra, focuses on 'harmony and motion in many different layers'. Karita Mattila sings two striking pieces by Sibelius, *Höstkväll* ('Autumn Evening'), a dramatic setting of Swedish words, and the tone-poem *Luonnotar*, written in 1913 for the Finnish soprano Aïno Ackté.

SATURDAY 10 AUGUST

7.30pm *ending at approximately 9.40pm*

Debussy
Printemps   16

Rakhmaninov
Rhapsody on a Theme of Paganini   24

INTERVAL

Sibelius
Lemminkäinen Suite
(Four Lemminkäinen Legends)   50

Olli Mustonen *piano*

Finnish Radio Symphony Orchestra
Jukka-Pekka Saraste *conductor*

Sibelius's sequence of four tone-poems depicting scenes from the life of Lemminkäinen, the warrior-adventurer of the Finnish national epic, the *Kalevala*, dates from between 1893 and 1895. Lemminkäinen first woos and wins the beautiful maiden Kyllikki, is murdered and descends into Tuonela, the Finnish Land of the Dead, is miraculously resurrected, and finally returns to the frozen forests of his Northern homeland. Though a product of sunnier climes, Debussy's early (1897) orchestral work *Printemps* ('Spring') – written while he was an unwilling laureate of the Prix de Rome – also encapsulates the joy of rebirth. The young Finnish pianist Olli Mustonen makes his Prom debut in Rakhmaninov's popular Rhapsody.

SUNDAY 11 AUGUST

7.30pm *ending at approximately 9.35pm*

Britten
Cantata Misericordium   21

Bach
Concerto in C minor for Violin
and Oboe, after BWV 1060   14

INTERVAL

Lennox Berkeley
Divertimento in B flat major   18

Mozart
Mass in C major, K257 'Credo'   30

Celia Nicklin *oboe*
Tom Bowes *violin*

Joan Rodgers *soprano*
Michael Chance *counter-tenor*
Maldwyn Davies *tenor*
David Wilson-Johnson *bass*

BBC Singers
London Mozart Players
Jane Glover *conductor*

A judicious mix of eighteenth- and twentieth-century choral and instrumental music. Mozart's 'Credo' Mass, written two months before his twenty-first birthday, is one of a group of short masses intended to please his austere employer, the Archbishop of Salzburg, whose requirements stipulated that an entire Mass should last no longer than three-quarters of an hour.

MONDAY 12 AUGUST

7.30pm *ending at approximately 9.30pm*

Pre-Prom talk at 6.15pm
Martin Butler

Tchaikovsky
Marche slave   10

Martin Butler
O Rio
BBC commission: world premiere   15

Liszt
Hunnenschlacht   16

INTERVAL

Prokofiev
Alexander Nevsky   38

Jean Rigby *mezzo-soprano*

Philharmonia Chorus
BBC Symphony Chorus
BBC Symphony Orchestra
Matthias Bamert *conductor*

Liszt's *Battle of the Huns* was inspired by an ambitious but artistically second-rate fresco by Wilhelm von Kaulbach (1805–74) depicting the gory clash between the forces of Attila the Hun and the Emperor Theodoric in 451. Liszt conducted the first performance in Weimar in 1857. Prokofiev fashioned his cantata from his music to Eisenstein's famous film (1938), culminating in the dramatic 'Battle on the Ice' between thirteenth-century Teutonic and Russian armies. Anthony Burton introduces Martin Butler's *O Rio* on page 34.

TUESDAY 13 AUGUST

7.30pm *ending at approximately 9.35pm*

Elgar
Cello Concerto in E minor   30

INTERVAL

Suk
Asrael Symphony   62

Ralph Kirshbaum *cello*

Royal Liverpool Philharmonic Orchestra
Libor Pešek *conductor*

Under Libor Pešek, its Music Director for the past four years, the Royal Liverpool Philharmonic Orchestra has undertaken a series of recordings featuring Czech music, including a cycle of Dvořák symphonies, Smetana's *Má Vlast*, and a major work by Josef Suk (1874–1935): his 'Asrael' Symphony (1905–6). 'Asrael' is the name of the angel who conducts the spirits of the dead, and this eloquent orchestral masterpiece was inspired by the deaths in quick succession of Suk's much-loved teacher Dvořák, and Dvořák's daughter Otilie (Suk's own young wife). Czech music specialist John Tyrrell compares *Asrael* to the symphonies of Mahler in terms of its 'structural mastery and emotional impact'.

WEDNESDAY 14 AUGUST

7.00pm *ending at approximately 9.15pm*

Henri Dutilleux
Mystère de l'instant   15

Beethoven
Piano Concerto No. 3 in C minor   35

INTERVAL

Tchaikovsky
Symphony No. 6 in B minor 'Pathétique'   47

John Lill *piano*

Royal Liverpool Philharmonic Orchestra
Libor Pešek *conductor*

No pianist can have explored the piano canon of Beethoven more thoroughly than John Lill: he was the first British pianist to perform all the Beethoven sonatas at both the South Bank and the Barbican; his complete sonata cycle has been broadcast by the BBC, and the complete concertos televised with the BBC Welsh Symphony Orchestra. Lill is currently re-recording the concertos, this time with the CBSO and Walter Weller. Dutilleux's *Mystère de l'instant* was commissioned by Paul Sacher and first performed in Zurich two years ago. The ninth of this sequence of 'snapshots in sound' is a 'Metamorphosis' on the name SACHER.

WEDNESDAY 14 AUGUST

10.00pm *ending at approximately 11.15pm*

31

Rakhmaninov
All-Night Vigil (Vespers)   67

USSR Ministry of Culture Chamber Choir
Valery Polyansky *conductor*

Rakhmaninov's *Vespers*, a setting of the liturgy for the *All-Night Vigil* which begins with Vespers on Saturday evening and lasts through to Matins on Sunday morning, was composed in 1915, and first performed in Moscow at a concert to raise funds for the war effort. It is scored for unaccompanied choir, since instrumental accompaniment is not permitted by the Orthodox Church. The *Vespers* were first broadcast in this country from a 1978 Prom performance given in Westminster Cathedral.

THURSDAY 15 AUGUST

7.30pm *ending at approximately 9.30pm*

32

Berlioz
Overture 'Beatrice and Benedict'   8

Shostakovich
Concerto for Piano, Trumpet and Strings   22

INTERVAL

Schubert
Symphony No. 9 'Great C major'   54

David Owen Norris *piano*
Nigel Boddice *trumpet*

BBC Scottish Symphony Orchestra
Takuo Yuasa *conductor*

The ebullient soloist, accompanist and broadcaster David Owen Norris is joined by Nigel Boddice, principal trumpet of the BBC Scottish Symphony Orchestra, in Shostakovich's First Piano Concerto. Unlike his other concertos, this was a relatively early work, written in 1933, just after the completion of the Twenty-Four Preludes for piano. The composer himself gave the Moscow premiere, and the piece was first heard in this country at a 1936 BBC Winter Prom in the Queen's Hall, when Eileen Joyce and Herbert Barr played it under Sir Henry Wood.

FRIDAY 16 AUGUST

7.30pm *ending at approximately 9.15pm*

33

Dvořák
The Spectre's Bride   90

Judith Howarth *soprano*
David Kuebler *tenor*
Peter Mikulaš *baritone*

BBC Symphony Chorus
USSR Ministry of Culture Chamber Choir
BBC Symphony Orchestra
Gennady Rozhdestvensky *conductor*

Dvořák, whose 150th birthday is celebrated in this year's Proms, was first invited to England by the Philharmonic Society following the success of his *Stabat Mater* here. After three triumphant concerts of his own works in London, he was commissioned to write substantial choral pieces for the Birmingham and Leeds festivals, plus a new symphony (the Seventh) for the Philharmonic Society. The Birmingham work turned out to be the dramatic cantata *The Spectre's Bride*, which received a rapturous reception at its first British performance in 1885. Gennady Rozhdestvensky has proved a tireless champion not only of contemporary music, but also of the lesser-known classics.

NB There will be no interval in this performance

SATURDAY 17 AUGUST

7.30pm *ending at approximately 9.45pm*

Pre-Prom talk at 6.15pm
Martin Dalby

Martin Dalby
The Mary Bean
BBC commission: world premiere   15

Mendelssohn
Piano Concerto No. 1 in G minor   20

INTERVAL

Rakhmaninov
Symphony No. 2 in E minor   56

Moura Lympany *piano*

Royal Scottish National Orchestra
Sir Alexander Gibson *conductor*

In January this year the Scottish National Orchestra received the prefix 'Royal' in recognition of its centenary. Sir Alexander Gibson has celebrated a record twenty-five seasons both as Music Director (now Conductor Laureate) of Scottish Opera, and also as Music Director of the SNO, with which he has toured widely and made many award-winning recordings. Moura Lympany, who celebrates her own seventy-fifth birthday the day after this concert, joins the orchestra in Mendelssohn's popular First Concerto – in which she made her public debut at the age of twelve.

SUNDAY 18 AUGUST

7.30pm *ending at approximately 9.45pm*

Purcell
Hail! bright Cecilia
(Ode for St Cecilia's Day, 1692)   52

INTERVAL

Telemann
Ouverture in C major ('Wassermusik')   24

Handel
Musick for the Royal Fireworks   21

Gillian Fisher *soprano*
James Bowman *counter-tenor*
Rogers Covey-Crump *tenor*
Charles Daniels *tenor*
Michael George *baritone*
Simon Keenlyside *bass*

The Choir of the King's Consort
The King's Consort
Robert King *director*

Following their recent much-commended recording of the *Musick for the Royal Fireworks* in Handel's original scoring, The King's Consort under Robert King presents the first live performance since 1749 to use Handel's full quota of period instruments, in this spectacular (and no doubt noisy!) Prom. Purcell's last and most perfect *Ode for St Cecilia's Day* and Telemann's *Water Music* for a special occasion in Hamburg complete a programme of the finest Baroque ceremonial music.

MONDAY 19 AUGUST

6.00pm *ending at approximately 7.15pm*

Janet Owen Thomas
Rosaces
UK premiere   8

Bach
Toccata and Fugue in D minor,
BWV 538 'Dorian'   13

Brian Ferneyhough
Sieben Sterne   15

Reubke
Sonata in C minor 'The 94th Psalm'   24

Kevin Bowyer *organ*

Winner of five major international competitions, Kevin Bowyer – at the age of only thirty – commands one of the largest repertoires of any organist today, and has recently undertaken a massive recording project, including the complete organ works of Bach. Brian Ferneyhough's *Sieben Sterne* (*Seven Stars*), was commissioned by Radio Berne in 1970, and first performed at the 1974 Royan Festival. Requiring two assistants in performance, it is eminently suited to the Royal Albert Hall's majestic organ. Janet Owen Thomas was born in Crosby in 1961 and went to St Hugh's College, Oxford, where she studied with Robert Saxton and Nicholas Danby. 'Rosaces', she says, 'is in the form of a free fantasia, and reflects 'the changing colours, themes and textures which appear in a rose window.' The work dates from 1984.

MONDAY 19 AUGUST
8.00pm *ending at approximately 10.15pm*

Brahms
Piano Concerto No. 1 in D minor   48

INTERVAL

Musorgsky orch. various
Pictures at an Exhibition   55

Emanuel Ax *piano*

The Philharmonia
Leonard Slatkin *conductor*

Leonard Slatkin will introduce this unique version of Musorgsky's *Pictures*, which draws on the work of nine different orchestrators: Ravel, Henry Wood, Vladimir Ashkenazy, Lucien Cailliet, Sergey Gorchakov, Lawrence Leonard, Leonidas Leonardi, Leopold Stokowski and Mikhail Tushmalov. 'The version we are presenting is not meant as an indication of who is best', says Slatkin, 'rather it is an attempt to show that there are limitless possibilities in a work that many of us have come to take for granted.' The Polish-born pianist Emanuel Ax, winner of the first Rubinstein Competition and now resident in New York, is the soloist in Brahms's First Concerto.

TUESDAY 20 AUGUST
7.30pm *ending at approximately 9.40pm*

Schumann
Cello Concerto in A minor   24

INTERVAL

Mahler
Symphony No. 5   71

Miklós Perényi *cello*

Gustav Mahler Jugendorchester
Claudio Abbado *conductor*

Founded in 1986 by Claudio Abbado, the Gustav Mahler Jugendorchester (based in Vienna) aimed to bring together young musicians from both sides of the Iron Curtain. Its task has become easier over the past eighteen months, and last year it became the first international youth orchestra to hold open auditions in Czechoslovakia, the former GDR and the Soviet Union. The orchestra meets twice a year for a rehearsal period followed by an international tour. Hungarian cellist Miklós Perényi is the soloist in Schumann's Cello Concerto. Mahler's Fifth Symphony, begun exactly ninety years ago this summer, has always been one of his most popular works.

WEDNESDAY 21 AUGUST
7.00pm *ending at approximately 9.15pm*

Haydn
Symphony No. 47 in G major   24

Brian Elias
Five Songs to Poems by
Irina Ratushinskaya   27

INTERVAL

Brahms
Symphony No. 1 in C minor   44

Mary King *mezzo-soprano*

BBC Symphony Orchestra
Lothar Zagrosek *conductor*

Mezzo-soprano Mary King, currently achieving international recognition for her outstanding commitment to contemporary vocal music, is the soloist in Brian Elias's *Five Songs to Poems by Irina Ratushinskaya* (the poet talks to Gerard McBurney on page 100). Haydn's Forty-Seventh Symphony, written when he was forty, is one of the best-known of his 'middle-period' works, incorporating the famous 'Menuet al roverso' – a Minuet and Trio designed to be playable both forwards and backwards.

WEDNESDAY 21 AUGUST

10.00pm *ending at approximately 11.10pm*

Mozart
Symphony No. 29 in A major, K201   24

Webern
Five Movements, Op. 5
(version for string orchestra)   4

Suk
Serenade for Strings   26

Orpheus Chamber Orchestra

Founded in New York nearly twenty years ago, the 26-piece Orpheus Chamber Orchestra has proved a highly successful experiment in orchestral democracy. Not only is there no conductor, but all members participate in essential decision-making and a different leader is elected for each piece! Webern's Five Movements (originally for string quartet) are early pieces, written in 1909 under the tutelage of Schoenberg, and revised twenty years later. Brahms personally recommended the publication of Josef Suk's attractive Serenade (1892), one of his first successes.

THURSDAY 22 AUGUST

7.30pm *ending at approximately 10.00pm*

Prokofiev
The Fiery Angel
Acts 1 & 2   60
INTERVAL
Acts 3–5   65

Ruprecht Sergey Leiferkus *baritone*
Hostess Felicity Palmer *mezzo-soprano*
Renata Galina Gorchakova *soprano*
Porter/Mathias Brian Bannatyne-Scott
  baritone
Fortune Teller Ann Howard *mezzo-soprano*
Jakob Glock/Doctor Francis Egerton *tenor*
Agrippa von Nettesheim Ian Caley *tenor*
Mephistopheles Robert Tear *tenor*
Faust Donald Maxwell *baritone*
The Inquisitor Mikhail Krutikov *bass*

BBC Singers
BBC Philharmonic
Edward Downes *conductor*

It is most appropriate that Edward Downes's last Prom as Principal Conductor of the BBC Philharmonic should be a concert performance of a Prokofiev opera: he is equally distinguished as a musicologist specialising in the Russian repertoire, and some years ago completed Prokofiev's early opera *Maddalena* from the composer's unfinished manuscript. Christopher Palmer celebrates Prokofiev's centenary and introduces *The Fiery Angel* on page 20.

FRIDAY 23 AUGUST

7.30pm *ending at approximately 9.30pm*

Weber
Overture 'Euryanthe'   8

Brahms
Violin Concerto in D major   40
INTERVAL

Bartók
Concerto for Orchestra   38

Dmitry Sitkovetsky *violin*

BBC Philharmonic
Yan Pascal Tortelier *conductor*

A programme with two concertos – one in which the orchestra plays its traditional role, and another in which all sections of the orchestra are given an equal chance to shine as soloists. This is Yan Pascal Tortelier's first Prom as Principal Conductor Designate of the BBC Philharmonic (he takes over from Edward Downes at the beginning of the 1992–3 season). Gerald Larner talks to him on page 82. Dmitry Sitkovetsky, arguably the most exceptionally talented violinist of his generation to emerge from the Soviet Union, is planning to record the Brahms concerto, together with those of Beethoven, Mendelssohn, Elgar and Bartók.

SATURDAY 24 AUGUST

7.30pm *ending at approximately 9.45pm*

Shostakovich
Symphony No. 8 in C minor 60

INTERVAL

Debussy
La Mer 21

Skryabin
The Poem of Ecstasy 19

European Community Youth Orchestra
Vladimir Ashkenazy *conductor*

The European Community Youth Orchestra's account of Bruckner's Eighth Symphony under Bernard Haitink was one of the highlights of the 1989 Prom season. Here they return under Vladimir Ashkenazy in an enterprising programme, beginning with the second of Shostakovich's trilogy of war symphonies, written within a two-month space in 1943. 'My new work is an attempt to look into the future, to the post-war era', said Shostakovich. 'The philosophical concept can be summed up in three words: life is beautiful. All that is dark and evil rots away, and beauty triumphs.'

SUNDAY 25 AUGUST

7.00pm *ending at approximately 9.50pm*

Mozart
La clemenza di Tito *(semi-staged)*

Act I 67

INTERVAL

Act 2 71

Glyndebourne Festival Opera

Tito Philip Langridge *tenor*
Vitellia Ashley Putnam *soprano*
Servilia Elzbieta Szmytka *soprano*
Sesto Diana Montague *mezzo-soprano*
Annio Martine Mahe *mezzo-soprano*
Publio Peter Rose *bass*

Glyndebourne Chorus
The London Philharmonic
Andrew Davis *conductor*

After staging an all-Mozart season as part of the bicentennial celebrations, Glyndebourne Festival Opera under its Music Director, Andrew Davis, pays its annual visit to the Proms with Mozart's penultimate opera. Philip Langridge, who has sung the title-role of *Idomeneo* at La Scala and at Covent Garden, sings the Emperor Titus, while Diana Montague repeats her triumphant debuts at the New York Met and the 1989 Salzburg Festival as Sextus. American soprano Ashley Putnam, a memorable Arabella at Glyndebourne, made her Covent Garden debut five years ago as Jenůfa. Her wide repertoire includes many Mozart roles. Andrew Huth discusses *La clemenza di Tito* on page 14.

MONDAY 26 AUGUST

3.00pm *ending at approximately 4.50pm*

Brahms
Variations on the St Anthony Chorale 17

Mendelssohn
Violin Concerto in E minor 25

INTERVAL

Dvořák
Slavonic Dances, Op. 46 35

Joshua Bell *violin*

BBC Symphony Orchestra
Lothar Zagrosek *conductor*

Since his sensational debut at the age of fourteen with the Philadelphia Orchestra under Riccardo Muti, Joshua Bell has quickly reached the top flight of international violinists. This season he is working with the Cleveland, Philharmonia and Washington National Symphony orchestras, as well as making this keenly-anticipated Prom appearance. Dvořák's *Slavonic Dances* represent the composer at his most personal and characteristic: rhythmic exuberance and richly expressive melodic vitality have ensured his lasting popularity. Brahms called his Variations 'on a theme by Haydn' – but musicology has demonstrated that the theme was, in fact, by someone else!

MONDAY 26 AUGUST

8.00pm *ending at approximately 10.20pm*

Brahms
Piano Concerto No. 2 in B flat major   49

INTERVAL

Mahler
Symphony No. 4 in G major   57

Alfred Brendel *piano*

Cheryl Studer *soprano*

Berlin Philharmonic Orchestra
Claudio Abbado *conductor*

Claudio Abbado makes his second appearance this season, this time as Chief Conductor of the celebrated Berlin Philharmonic Orchestra, making its first ever visit to the Proms. Alfred Brendel, a frequent and popular soloist in the series, plays Brahms's Second Concerto, one of the longest and most demanding in the repertory, while Cheryl Studer, fresh from recent successes in Verdi roles at La Scala, makes her Prom debut in the finale of Mahler's enchanting Fourth Symphony.

TUESDAY 27 AUGUST

7.30pm *ending at approximately 9.35pm*

Beethoven
Overture 'Egmont'   9

Berg
Seven Early Songs   17

INTERVAL

Bruckner
Symphony No. 7 in E major   64

Felicity Lott *soprano*

The London Philharmonic
Franz Welser-Möst *conductor*

Felicity Lott is closely identified with the music of Richard Strauss. Her interpretation of the Four Last Songs has won wide acclaim, and this season she made her debuts at the New York Met as the Marschallin, and at the Vienna State Opera as Arabella. Tonight she forsakes Strauss for Berg's equally ecstatic and lyrical settings of love poems, written in his early twenties, and dedicated to his wife Helene. The dynamic young Austrian conductor Franz Welser-Möst has been the London Philharmonic's Chief Conductor since September 1990.

WEDNESDAY 28 AUGUST

7.30pm *ending at approximately 9.35pm*

Poulenc
Gloria   28

Bridge
Phantasm   25

INTERVAL

Walton
Belshazzar's Feast   35

Lilian Watson *soprano*

Kathryn Stott *piano*

John Tomlinson *bass*

London Symphony Chorus
BBC Welsh Symphony Orchestra
Richard Hickox *conductor*

Lancastrian-born Kathryn Stott shot to fame at nineteen, when, as a student at the Royal College of Music, she became the first British woman to win a prize in the Leeds International Piano Competition. In her fifth Prom appearance she tackles an important but little-known work by Bridge (see page 26). Poulenc's *Gloria* (1959) is a late work, written after he had renewed his ties with Catholicism. A startling mixture of sincere religious fervour and sheer *joie-de-vivre*, the *Gloria* was partly inspired by 'those frescoes in which angels stick their tongues out' and by the sight of some 'solemn Benedictine monks playing football'.

THURSDAY 29 AUGUST

7.30pm *ending at approximately 9.35pm*

Sir Michael Tippett
Concerto for Double String Orchestra 24

Glazunov
Violin Concerto in A minor 21

INTERVAL

Walton
Symphony No. 1 44

Kurt Nikkanen *violin*

Royal Philharmonic Orchestra
Vladimir Ashkenazy *conductor*

Still in his early twenties, Kurt Nikkanen is one of the USA's most dazzling virtuosos, widely admired not only for his astounding technique but also for his mature interpretative insight. He made his debut three years ago in the Glazunov concerto with the Cleveland Orchestra under Vladimir Ashkenazy. His London debut last November, this time with Ashkenazy and the Royal Philharmonic Orchestra, preceded a highly successful European tour. He has just made his first record – of the Tchaikovsky and Glazunov concertos with the London Philharmonic under Yuri Simonov. Diana McVeagh writes about Walton and Tippett on page 26.

FRIDAY 30 AUGUST

7.30pm *ending at approximately 9.30pm*

Pre-Prom talk at 6.15pm
Peter Paul Nash

Peter Paul Nash
Symphony
BBC commission: world premiere 25

Britten
Serenade for Tenor, Horn and Strings 23

INTERVAL

Sir Harrison Birtwistle
Earth Dances 37

Ian Caley *tenor*
Michael Thompson *horn*

BBC Symphony Orchestra
Peter Eötvös *conductor*

The versatile Peter Eötvös – conductor, composer, co-editor of the new complete Bartók edition and one of the world's leading exponents of contemporary music – returns to the BBC Symphony Orchestra, of which he was Principal Guest Conductor from 1985 to 1989, in Birtwistle's cathartic orchestral masterpiece. Virtuoso horn-player Michael Thompson partners Ian Caley in Britten's haunting Serenade. Peter Paul Nash's new work is introduced by Anthony Burton on page 34.

SPECIAL OFFER!

SATURDAY 31 AUGUST

7.30pm *ending at approximately 9.40pm*

Cherubini
Pas redoublés and Marches for the
Prussian Garrison of Paris – selection 8

Félicien David
Nonet in C minor 18

London Gabrieli Brass Ensemble
Christopher Larkin *conductor*

INTERVAL

Beethoven
Symphony No. 9 in D minor 'Choral' 69

Jane Eaglen *soprano*
Kathleen Kuhlmann *mezzo-soprano*
Anthony Rolfe Johnson *tenor*
John Tomlinson *bass*

London Philharmonic Choir
The London Philharmonic
Klaus Tennstedt *conductor*

This year's Ninth falls to the London Philharmonic's distinguished Conductor Laureate, Klaus Tennstedt – whose performance of Beethoven's Fifth at last year's Proms was hailed as 'a reading of mind-bending originality'. Cherubini's set of quicksteps and marches was written in 1814 for the Paris-based band of the King of Prussia's Rifle Regiment. Félicien David (1810–76), best-known for his concert works and operas on fashionable Oriental subjects, wrote two nonets for brass instruments, of which only the second (1839) survives.

Beethoven
Piano Concerto No. 5 in E flat major
'Emperor'   39
INTERVAL
Shostakovich
Symphony No. 10   49

Philippe Bianconi *piano*

Orchestre de Paris
Semyon Bychkov *conductor*

Russian-born Semyon Bychkov succeeded Daniel
Barenboim as Music Director of the Orchestre de
Paris two years ago. Resident for the last decade
in the refurbished Salle Pleyel, the orchestra has
recently embarked on a diverse and ambitious
recording schedule, including works by Bizet,
Franck, Rakhmaninov and Stravinsky. Since win-
ning the silver medal in the seventh Van Cliburn
International Competition, Philippe Bianconi has
been much in demand as a soloist and recitalist,
especially in the USA.

Kodály
Dances of Galánta   16
Henri Dutilleux
Symphony No. 2   29
INTERVAL
Strauss
Also sprach Zarathustra   34

Orchestre de Paris
Semyon Bychkov *conductor*

The French composer Henri Dutilleux (born in
1916) cannot be categorised: his works do not
belong to any 'school' and he remains an enig-
matic nonconformist, crafting a small but highly
personal output of extreme sensibility. His Second Symphony dates from 1958–9. Scored for
two orchestral groups of unequal size – a large
orchestra and a small chamber group of twelve
players – it explores the possibilities offered by
polytonality and polyrhythm, within the framework of variation technique.

Bridge
Enter Spring   20
Ravel
Piano Concerto in G   22
INTERVAL
Vaughan Williams
Symphony No. 2
'A London Symphony'   45

Artur Pizarro *piano*

BBC Symphony Orchestra
David Atherton *conductor*

Ever modest and self-deprecating, Vaughan Williams felt that his early training had not equipped
him sufficiently for the life of a professional composer. In his mid-thirties he tried to refine his
technique by taking lessons from that master
of the orchestral palette, Ravel. *A London Symphony* reflects his new-found confidence. Artur
Pizarro, sensational winner of the 1990 Harveys
Leeds International Competition, and now an
established top-rank international soloist, makes
his Prom debut in Ravel's own exquisite concerto, one of his last major compositions.

TUESDAY 3 SEPTEMBER

10.00pm *ending at approximately 11.15pm*

Victoria
Motet and Mass 'O Quam Gloriosum' 25

Alonso Lobo
Ave Maria 6

Juan Gutiérrez de Padilla
Salve Regina 8

Francisco Guerrero
Ave, Virgo Sanctissima 5

Regina Caeli 4

Victoria
Vidi Speciosam 7

Westminster Cathedral Choir
James O'Donnell *director*

A programme of Spanish liturgical music from the High Renaissance. The two greatest Iberian composers of their time, Victoria and Guerrero worked respectively in Rome (subsequently at a Madrid convent), and at Seville Cathedral, while Alonso Lobo, Guerrero's pupil and assistant, was esteemed 'as an equal' by Victoria. Juan Gutiérrez de Padilla began his career at the cathedrals of Málaga and Cádiz before sailing for the New World. He spent the last forty-or-so years of his life as maestro at Puebla Cathedral in Mexico.

SPECIAL OFFER!

WEDNESDAY 4 SEPTEMBER

7.30pm *ending at approximately 9.25pm*

Sofia Gubaidulina
Offertorium 36

INTERVAL

Prokofiev
Symphony No. 5 in B flat major 44

Gidon Kremer *violin*

City of Birmingham Symphony Orchestra
Simon Rattle *conductor*

Simon Rattle and the CBSO have a full diary this year, including a tour of the Far East and the inauguration of the orchestra's new Birmingham home, Symphony Hall, in June. Gidon Kremer, an artist who prizes communication and integrity over and above the glamour of international acclaim, joins the orchestra in Sofia Gubaidulina's *Offertorium* (its composer is sixty in October). Effectively a concerto written for Kremer, *Offertorium* (1980) takes as its focal point the theme which Frederick the Great gave to Bach and which formed the basis of his own *Musical Offering*. The piece is also concerned with the idea of sacrifice, as the theme itself is 'sacrificed' through its transformation and disappearance.

THURSDAY 5 SEPTEMBER

8.00pm *ending at approximately 9.25pm*

Mahler
Symphony No. 9 75

City of Birmingham Symphony Orchestra
Simon Rattle *conductor*

Simon Rattle's 1987 recording of Mahler's 'Resurrection' Symphony with the CBSO won three awards, including *Gramophone*'s Record of the Year. Here they tackle the monumental Ninth Symphony, Mahler's superstitious but vain attempt to cheat death by pretending it was really his 'Tenth'. 'The first movement is the most heavenly thing Mahler ever wrote' was Alban Berg's verdict. 'It expresses a deep love for this earth, the longing to live in peace on it, to enjoy nature to the full – before death comes.'

FRIDAY 6 SEPTEMBER

7.30pm *ending at approximately 9.30pm*

Pre-Prom talk at 6.15pm
Sir Michael Tippett

Bridge
Overture 'Rebus'   10

Sir Michael Tippett
Byzantium
European premiere   21

INTERVAL

Ravel
Daphnis and Chloë   55

Faye Robinson *soprano*

BBC Symphony Chorus
BBC Symphony Orchestra
Andrew Davis *conductor*

Another little-known work by Frank Bridge draws attention to the extraordinary talents of this underrated composer fifty years after his death. *Rebus* (the title might be defined as a hieroglyphic riddle) was completed only five months before Bridge's death, and premiered by Sir Henry Wood in February 1941. Anthony Burton discusses Tippett's new work on page 34. Though largely shorn of its original erotic impetus, the scenario eventually agreed between Ravel and the choreographer Fokine for the one-act ballet *Daphnis and Chloë* inspired one of the composer's most ravishing orchestral scores.

SATURDAY 7 SEPTEMBER

8.00pm *ending at approximately 9.55pm*

NOTE TIME

Beethoven
Symphony No. 8 in F major   26

INTERVAL

Berlioz
Symphonie fantastique   54

Boston Symphony Orchestra
Seiji Ozawa *conductor*

The Boston Symphony Orchestra, which celebrates its 110th anniversary this season, initiated the idea of 'Promenade' concerts even before Sir Henry Wood: the first Boston 'Prom' – soon to develop into the famous 'Boston Pops' – took place in July 1885. Now in his eighteenth year as Music Director, Seiji Ozawa has taken his virtuoso ensemble on tour throughout the USA, Europe and Japan (revisited this season for the fourth time), and has greatly expanded its recording activities, in addition to maintaining a schedule of over 250 concerts a year.

SUNDAY 8 SEPTEMBER

3.00pm *ending at approximately 4.30pm*

NOTE TIME

Children's Prom
Prokofiev
Winter Bonfire   19

Witold Lutoslawski
Three Children's Songs   10

Prokofiev
The Ugly Duckling   12

Britten
Three Two-Part Songs   10

Prokofiev
Peter and the Wolf   21

Penelope Walmsley-Clark *soprano*

Dame Judi Dench *narrator*

Finchley Children's Music Group
New London Orchestra
Ronald Corp *conductor*

Following the huge success of *Noye's Fludde* last season, the Finchley Children's Music Group, under their director Ronald Corp, return in a programme of twentieth-century classics. Judi Dench, one of Britain's best-loved stage and screen personalities, relates the tale of *Peter and the Wolf*, while two lesser-known works from the opposite ends of Prokofiev's career – his early setting of the famous Hans Christian Andersen story, and *Winter Bonfire*, a late work for children's chorus and small orchestra – frame songs by Lutoslawski and Britten.

SUNDAY 8 SEPTEMBER

8.00pm *ending at approximately 10.05pm*

Mozart
Symphony No. 31 in D major, K297
'Paris'   18

Schubert
Symphony No. 6 in C major   31

INTERVAL

Dvořák
Symphony No. 7 in D minor   40

Dresden Staatskapelle
Sir Colin Davis *conductor*

Acclaimed at various times as 'the best orchestra in the world' by such connoisseurs as Rousseau, Beethoven and Richard Strauss, the Dresden Staatskapelle is one of the world's most venerable orchestral institutions, tracing its foundation back to 1548. Throughout its history as a concert and opera orchestra, it can claim among its distinguished list of musical directors Heinrich Schütz, Hasse, Weber, Wagner (three of whose operas it premiered), Fritz Busch, Karl Böhm, Rudolf Kempe, Kurt Sanderling and Herbert Blomstedt. Since the mid-nineteenth century the orchestra's annual concert season has attracted record audiences, and in recent years it has recorded a wide-ranging repertoire under the world's finest conductors, including Sir Colin Davis.

MONDAY 9 SEPTEMBER

7.30pm *ending at approximately 9.30pm*

Mendelssohn
Overture 'The Hebrides'
('Fingal's Cave')   10

Beethoven
Symphony No. 4 in B flat major   34

INTERVAL

Reger
Variations and Fugue on
a Theme of Hiller   39

Dresden Staatskapelle
Sir Colin Davis *conductor*

Max Reger died at the age of only forty-three, but his output – much of it little-known outside Germany – is vast. He worked under enormous pressure, once writing to a friend: 'Remember Mendelssohn, Mozart, Schubert, Wolf – we have so little time left, and I must finish my work'. Variation form proved central to his oeuvre, and his Op. 100, an orchestral set of massive proportions culminating in a mighty fugue, is based on a 'merry theme' by the eighteenth-century German composer Johann Adam Hiller.

TUESDAY 10 SEPTEMBER

7.30pm *ending at approximately 9.30pm*

Pre-Prom talk at 6.15pm
Hugh Wood

Schubert
Symphony No. 3 in D major   23

Hugh Wood
Piano Concerto
BBC commission: world premiere   25

INTERVAL

Nielsen
Symphony No. 5   35

Joanna MacGregor *piano*

BBC Symphony Orchestra
Andrew Davis *conductor*

Joanna MacGregor studied music with Hugh Wood at Cambridge before embarking on a pianistic career which has developed with astonishing speed over the past six years. A composer herself, with a strong interest in contemporary music, she made an auspicious debut in Ravel's Left Hand Concerto at last year's Proms. Schubert never heard a professional performance of his Third Symphony, written when he was eighteen. In fact, it lay neglected until August Manns conducted it at London's Crystal Palace in 1881. Nielsen's brooding Fifth Symphony – in which the side-drummer is instructed to 'improvise as if at all costs to destroy the music' – caused an uproar at its Stockholm premiere in 1924.

WEDNESDAY 11 SEPTEMBER

7.30pm *ending at approximately 10.00pm*

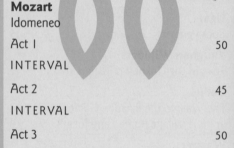

Mozart (reconstructed Levin)
Sinfonia Concertante in E flat major
for flute, oboe, horn and bassoon,
K297B   30

Mozart
Piano Concerto No. 20 in D minor,
K466   30

INTERVAL

Kommet her, ihr frechen Sünder   4

Vado, ma dove?   5

Voi avete un cor fedele   6

Symphony No. 41 in C major, K551
'Jupiter'   34

William Bennett *flute*
Neil Black *oboe*
Robin O'Neill *bassoon*
Frank Lloyd *horn*

Mitsuko Uchida *piano*

Ann Murray *mezzo-soprano*

English Chamber Orchestra
George Cleve *conductor*

An all-Mozart programme conducted by one
of the USA's Mozart specialists. The Sinfonia
Concertante for wind is heard in a newly reconstructed version by the American musicologist
Robert Levin which is as close to Mozart's lost
original as we are likely to get.

THURSDAY 12 SEPTEMBER

7.30pm *ending at approximately 9.40pm*

Stravinsky
Symphony in C   30
Symphony of Psalms   22

INTERVAL

Bernstein
Symphonic Dances
from 'West Side Story'   22
Chichester Psalms   18

London Symphony Chorus
London Symphony Orchestra
Michael Tilson Thomas *conductor*

In 1988 Michael Tilson Thomas was appointed
Principal Conductor of the LSO, with which he
had made his London debut eighteen years earlier. Leonard Bernstein, too, was closely associated
with the LSO. His exultant settings of three
psalms for the 1965 Chichester Festival reveal a
fascinating amalgam of American popular culture
and Hebraic religious fervour, seasoned with a
dash of Anglicanism, while his exciting dance-
suite from *West Side Story* exemplifies his uncanny ability to entertain in a popular style while
maintaining the highest musical standards.

FRIDAY 13 SEPTEMBER

7.00pm *ending at approximately 10.25pm*

NOTE TIME

Mozart
Idomeneo
Act 1   50
INTERVAL
Act 2   45
INTERVAL
Act 3   50

Welsh National Opera

Idomeneo Dennis O'Neill *tenor*
Electra Suzanne Murphy *soprano*
Ilia Amanda Roocroft *soprano*
Idamante John Mark Ainsley *tenor*
Arbace Anthony Roden *tenor*

Orchestra and Chorus of Welsh National
Opera
Sir Charles Mackerras *conductor*

A privileged concert preview of Welsh National
Opera's forthcoming production of *Idomeneo*,
conducted by its Musical Director, Sir Charles
Mackerras. Dennis O'Neill, one of the world's
most sought-after tenors in a wide variety of
repertoire, takes the title-role, while the young
Lancastrian-born soprano Amanda Roocroft,
who appears this year as Pamina at Covent Garden and as Fiordiligi at Glyndebourne, sings the
Trojan princess Ilia. Andrew Huth writes about
Idomeneo on page 14.

SATURDAY 14 SEPTEMBER

7.30pm *ending at approximately 10.30pm*

67

Elgar
Cockaigne   15

Vaughan Williams
Toward the Unknown Region   12

Delius
The Walk to the Paradise Garden
from 'A Village Romeo and Juliet'   8

Wagner
Immolation Scene
from 'Götterdämmerung'   20

INTERVAL

Bliss
March from 'Things to Come'   4

Borodin
Polovtsian Dances from 'Prince Igor'   15

Trad arr. Goossens
The Last Rose of Summer   3

Elgar
Pomp and Circumstance March No. 1   6

Henry Wood
Fantasia on British Sea-Songs   12

Arne
Rule, Britannia!   5

Parry orch. Elgar
Jerusalem   2

Dame Gwyneth Jones *soprano*
Sidonie Goossens *harp*
BBC Singers
BBC Symphony Orchestra and Chorus
Andrew Davis *conductor*

HOW TO BOOK

By post
Postal booking for all concerts opens on **Wednesday 8 May**. Ticket applications cannot be dealt with before this date. Applications should be made on the booking form and posted to:

Promenade Concerts Box Office
Royal Albert Hall
London SW7 2AP

A fee of 50p will be added to cover postage and administration.

Payment
Visa and Access (MasterCard) only are accepted by the Royal Albert Hall. Please enter your credit card number in the box on the booking form.

Cheques and postal orders should be made payable to *Royal Albert Hall*. Your application will be handled more quickly, and the need for refunds avoided, if the amount of the cheque is *left blank*, with an upper limit stated.

Ticket availability and refunds
If the tickets you want are not available, lower-priced tickets for the same concert will be sent. Please tick the box on your booking form if this is **not** acceptable. Once bought, tickets cannot be exchanged for other performances, nor will refunds be made except in the event of a cancelled performance.

Booking by phone
Tickets will be available by phone from the Royal Albert Hall (071-823 9998) from **Monday 10 June**. The lines are open from 9am to 9pm seven days a week. A fee of 50p will be added to each telephone booking to cover postage and administration.

NB *Some concerts may be sold out by the time telephone/personal booking opens.*

Booking in person
Tickets will be on sale at the Royal Albert Hall from **Monday 10 June**. The Box Office is open from 9am to 9pm seven days a week.

The Royal Albert Hall has four spaces for concert-goers in wheelchairs. Please phone the Box Office (071-823 9998) before ordering tickets. To check availability during postal booking period ring 071-225 0765

Last Night
Subject to availability, up to two tickets per applicant will be allocated to those who apply at the same time for at least *five* other concerts in the 1991 season. (Please note that in the event of Last Night tickets being sold out, no refunds for other tickets purchased will be payable.)

Season tickets automatically include admission to the Arena or Gallery, as appropriate, on the Last Night. Remaining tickets for these areas will be sold on a first-come, first-served basis to Promenaders who have attended at least *five* other concerts. As proof of attendance, please attach the torn-off portion of your Promenade tickets to the booking form and present them at the Box Office as soon as possible.

Price Codes

Price code	Stalls	Loggia Boxes 8 seats / 2nd Tier Boxes 4 seats	Choir	Balcony	Balcony Restricted view
A	£13.00	£11.00	£9.00	£7.00	£3.50
B	£18.00	£14.50	£11.50	£8.00	£3.50
C	£35.00	£25.00	£15.00	£10.00	£4.00
D	£7.50	£7.50	£7.50	£4.50	£3.00
E	£42.00	£42.00	£28.00	£28.00	£14.00

Promenade Tickets
(available at the door only)

Arena	£2.50
Gallery	£2.00

Promenade Season Tickets

Arena *(whole season)*	£95.00
*(half season)**	£60.00
Gallery *(whole season)*	£70.00
*(half season)**	£40.00

*1st half: 19 July – 16 August, plus Last Night
2nd half: 17 August – 14 September

Season Tickets

Season tickets for the Arena and Gallery must be obtained by post from the Royal Albert Hall.

Please note:

– Only one season ticket per applicant will be issued.
– No duplicates will be issued against season tickets.
– Season tickets do not guarantee admission later than *ten minutes* before the concert starting-time.

ROYAL ALBERT HALL SEATING PLAN

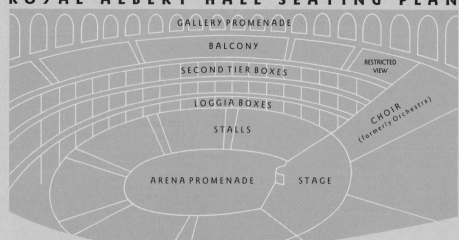

HOW TO GET THERE

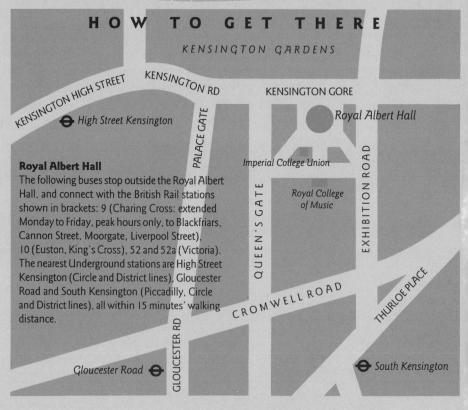

Royal Albert Hall
The following buses stop outside the Royal Albert Hall, and connect with the British Rail stations shown in brackets: 9 (Charing Cross: extended Monday to Friday, peak hours only, to Blackfriars, Cannon Street, Moorgate, Liverpool Street), 10 (Euston, King's Cross), 52 and 52a (Victoria). The nearest Underground stations are High Street Kensington (Circle and District lines), Gloucester Road and South Kensington (Piccadilly, Circle and District lines), all within 15 minutes' walking distance.

BOOKING FORM

PRICE CODES

A
Stalls £13.00 Loggia Boxes (8 seats) and 2nd Tier Boxes (4 seats) £11.00 Choir £9.00 Balcony £7.00 Balcony (*restricted view*) £3.50

B
Stalls £18.00 Loggia Boxes (8 seats) and 2nd Tier Boxes (4 seats) £14.50 Choir £11.50 Balcony £8.00 Balcony (*restricted view*) £3.50

C
Stalls £35.00 Loggia Boxes (8 seats) and 2nd Tier Boxes (4 seats) £25.00 Choir £15.00 Balcony £10.00 Balcony (*restricted view*) £4.00

D
Stalls £7.50 Loggia Boxes (8 seats) and 2nd Tier Boxes (4 seats) £7.50 Choir £7.50 Balcony £4.50 Balcony (*restricted view*) £3.00

E
Stalls £42.00 Loggia Boxes (8 seats) and 2nd Tier Boxes (4 seats) £42.00 Choir £28.00 Balcony £28.00 Balcony (*restricted view*) £14.00

Concert No.		Price code	No. of seats	Area	Total £	Office use
1	Friday 19 July 7.30	B				
2	Saturday 20 July 7.30	A				
3	Sunday 21 July 7.30	A				
4	Monday 22 July 7.30	A				
5	Tuesday 23 July 7.00	A		SPECIAL OFFER!		
6	Tuesday 23 July 10.00	D		SPECIAL OFFER!		
7	Wednesday 24 July 7.30	A				
8	Thursday 25 July 7.30	A				
9	Friday 26 July 7.00	A				
10	Friday 26 July 10.00	D				
11	Saturday 27 July 7.30	A				
12	Sunday 28 July 7.30	A				
13	Monday 29 July 7.30	A		SPECIAL OFFER!		
14	Tuesday 30 July 7.30	A				
15	Wednesday 31 July 7.30	A				
16	Thursday 1 August 7.30	A				
17	Friday 2 August 7.30	A				
18	Saturday 3 August 7.30	A				
19	Sunday 4 August 7.30	A				
20	Monday 5 August 7.30	A				
21	Tuesday 6 August 7.30	A				
22	Wednesday 7 August 7.00	A				
23	Wednesday 7 August 10.00	D		SPECIAL OFFER!		
24	Thursday 8 August 7.30	A		SPECIAL OFFER!		
25	Friday 9 August 7.30	A				
26	Saturday 10 August 7.30	A				
27	Sunday 11 August 7.30	A				
28	Monday 12 August 7.30	A		Choir off sale		
29	Tuesday 13 August 7.30	A				
30	Wednesday 14 August 7.00	A				
31	Wednesday 14 August 10.00	D				
32	Thursday 15 August 7.30	A				
33	Friday 16 August 7.30	A				
34	Saturday 17 August 7.30	A				
35	Sunday 18 August 7.30	A				
36	Monday 19 August 6.00	D				
				Total carried forward		

Complete this form (PLEASE USE BLOCK CAPITALS) and send it to:
Promenade Concerts Box Office, Royal Albert Hall, London SW7 2AP

Indicate method of payment below. DO NOT enclose s.a.e. Bookings will include a 50p charge to cover postage and administration.

☐ Debit my (VISA/ACCESS only) card no.

Expiry date _____

☐ I attach cheque/postal order made payable to **Royal Albert Hall** (please leave cheques open, with upper limit).

NAME _____

ADDRESS _____

Home address of cardholder (if different)

TELEPHONE (day) _____

(evening) _____

SIGNATURE _____

☐ **Do not** send lower-priced tickets
☐ Special Offer Voucher(s) enclosed

Concert No.		Price code	No. of seats	Area	Total £	Office use
				Total brought forward		
37	Monday 19 August 8.00	A				
38	Tuesday 20 August 7.30	A				
39	Wednesday 21 August 7.00	A				
40	Wednesday 21 August 10.00	D		⟨SPECIAL OFFER!⟩		
41	Thursday 22 August 7.30	A				
42	Friday 23 August 7.30	A				
43	Saturday 24 August 7.30	A				
44	Sunday 25 August 7.00	B				
45	Monday 26 August 3.00	A				
46	Monday 26 August 8.00	C				
47	Tuesday 27 August 7.30	A				
48	Wednesday 28 August 7.30	A				
49	Thursday 29 August 7.30	A				
50	Friday 30 August 7.30	A		⟨SPECIAL OFFER!⟩		
51	Saturday 31 August 7.30	B				
52	Sunday 1 September 7.30	B				
53	Monday 2 September 7.30	A				
54	Tuesday 3 September 7.00	A				
55	Tuesday 3 September 10.00	D		⟨SPECIAL OFFER!⟩		
56	Wednesday 4 September 7.30	A				
57	Thursday 5 September 8.00	A				
58	Friday 6 September 7.30	A				
59	Saturday 7 September 8.00	B				
60	Sunday 8 September 3.00	D				
61	Sunday 8 September 8.00	B				
62	Monday 9 September 7.30	B				
63	Tuesday 10 September 7.30	A				
64	Wednesday 11 September 7.30	A				
65	Thursday 12 September 7.30	A				
66	Friday 13 September 7.00	B				
67	Saturday 14 September 7.30	E				
	Arena Season *whole season*			£95.00		
	half season			£60.00 first half ☐ second half ☐		
	Gallery Season *whole season*			£70.00		
	half season			£40.00 first half ☐ second half ☐		
				Total		

NEW MUSIC AT THE PROMS

Save up to £4.00 on tickets for any of the Proms listed below which contain some of the season's contemporary music

Tuesday 23 July **Prom 5**
Monday 29 July **Prom 13**
Thursday 8 August **Prom 24**
Friday 30 August **Prom 50**

Send this voucher with your booking form (making the appropriate deduction to the total), or present it at the Royal Albert Hall Box Office (from 10 June) at time of purchase to claim your discount of **£2.00** off one ticket or **£4.00** off two tickets (not Promenade or Restricted View) for any one of the above concerts.

SPECIAL OFFERS

£2 NEW MUSIC VOUCHER

This voucher entitles the bearer to **£2.00** off one ticket or **£4.00** off two tickets for any one of the following Proms

Prom 5 23 July
Prom 13 29 July
Prom 24 8 August
Prom 50 30 August

NB Does not apply to Promenade or Restricted View tickets
Voucher valid at time of purchase only
Subject to availability

£4

LATE NIGHT MUSIC AT THE PROMS

Save £1.00 or £2.00 on tickets for any of the Late Night Proms listed below. All these concerts are at 10pm in the Royal Albert Hall.

Tuesday 23 July **Prom 6**
Wednesday 7 August **Prom 23**
Wednesday 21 August **Prom 40**
Tuesday 3 September **Prom 55**

Send this voucher with your booking form (making the appropriate deduction to the total), or present it at the Royal Albert Hall Box Office (from 10 June) at time of purchase to claim your discount of **£1.00** off one ticket or **£2.00** off two tickets (not Promenade or Restricted View) for any one of the above concerts.

£1 LATE NIGHT MUSIC VOUCHER

This voucher entitles the bearer to **£1.00** off one ticket or **£2.00** off two tickets for any one of the following Proms

Prom 6 23 July
Prom 23 7 August
Prom 40 21 August
Prom 55 3 September

NB Does not apply to Promenade or Restricted View tickets
Voucher valid at time of purchase only
Subject to availability

£2

BBC
CYMRU
WALES

VIENNA
PRAGUE
LEIPZIG
BERLIN
PARIS
TOKYO

BBC WELSH SYMPHONY ORCHESTRA

For details of the BBC Welsh Symphony Orchestra and Chorus 1991/92 season,
send your name and address, on a postcard to:
Huw Tregelles Williams, BBC, Llandaff, Cardiff CF5 2YQ.

BBC SYMPHONY ORCHESTRA

ALEX VON KOETTLITZ

The BBC Symphony Orchestra performs in fifteen concerts during this Prom Season and its Winter Season continues with concerts at the Royal Festival Hall from October to May. Conductors will include Andrew Davis, Pierre Boulez, David Atherton, Lothar Zagrosek, Oliver Knussen, Alexander Lazarev and Mark Wigglesworth.

For full details of the forthcoming season and to join the BBC Symphony Orchestra mailing list, please telephone 071–927 4714 or fill in the coupon and return to:

BBC Symphony Orchestra Mailing List
FREEPOST 17
London W1E 3HT
(no stamp required)

B B C

I would like to join the free BBC Symphony Orchestra Mailing List

Name _____

Address _____

_____

_____

Postcode _____

ANDREW DAVIS

in conversation with
Tess Knighton

RICHARD HOLT

Andrew Davis

ANDREW DAVIS'S FIRST ENCOUNTER with the BBC Symphony Orchestra was the stuff of every young conductor's wildest dreams. Called in at very short notice to replace Eliahu Inbal in what proved to be a triumphant performance of Janáček's *Glagolitic Mass* in November 1970, he has never looked back, in a career that has subsequently taken him all over the world. He has returned, however, to the point where it all started, taking up less than twenty years later the position of Chief Conductor of the BBC Symphony Orchestra, for which his respect and admiration in the meantime has only increased. Himself a musician with wide-ranging tastes, the orchestra's flexibility – its ability to turn with ease from Mozart to Mahler to Maw – holds a strong appeal for him, as indeed it did for his predecessor, Sir John Pritchard, and he sees it as his responsibility to keep this tradition alive. Perhaps the only drawback, as Davis points out, of such an all-embracing approach to the orchestral repertory, is that some of the core works are less regularly performed and therefore less familiar to some of the players: 'With this orchestra you can't assume that everyone will have played even something as well known as Beethoven's Fifth Symphony, which we did last season for the first time in several years!'

Davis also shares Sir John's concern for achieving beauty and refinement of orchestral sound, whatever the repertory, but perhaps even more especially in contemporary music, where he feels the BBC Symphony has a particularly significant contribution to make. 'This orchestra', he explains, 'can play contemporary music exceptionally well and has a major commitment to it. They can cope with it quickly, but in fact we have the advantage – the luxury, really – of having the time to prepare, to make those refinements of balance, colour and texture the music needs. It's one of the problems besetting the profession that insufficient rehearsal time

results in complex contemporary scores being worked on in a scramble to get the notes and rhythms right and not much more. I think it was George Szell who said about the Cleveland Orchestra that they started to rehearse where other orchestras left off. That sounds rather arrogant, but it would be our ideal.'

With never less than two full days of rehearsal for any one programme (and more, depending on the repertory to be rehearsed), Davis and the orchestra are able to bring this refinement to even the most demanding modern works. 'Berg said of his operas that they should be sung *bel canto*, and this is our aim – to bring out the beauty of every piece', adds Davis. This aim was clearly fulfilled in the performance of Tippett's *The Mask of Time* given last November as part of the orchestra's sixtieth-anniversary season, which the composer described as the best he had ever heard. In fact, Davis and the orchestra gave the European premiere of *The Mask of Time* at the 1984 Proms, and it is a work he particularly loves. This summer will see another European premiere of a new piece by Tippett at the Proms, the setting for soprano and orchestra of Yeats's poem *Byzantium* (Prom 58). Davis describes it as 'full of the amazing imagery that Tippett loves so much and that in his opera *New Year* [which Davis has just filmed at Glyndebourne] resulted in such new and original sounds. It's a big sing, dramatic and florid, and conceived with incredible inventiveness'.

Another premiere to be undertaken by Davis and the BBC Symphony Orchestra will be Hugh Wood's Piano Concerto, commissioned by the BBC and performed by Joanna MacGregor in Prom 63. Davis has long been an advocate of Wood's music, which he believes has been undeservedly neglected in recent years. Within the last eighteen months or so he has conducted several of Wood's major works, including the *Scenes from Comus*, the Cello Concerto and, in April of this year, the Symphony – another piece that originated as a Proms commission. Here Davis stresses the importance of second performances: 'After the excitement and attention attracted by a premiere, it's very disheartening for composers when they find it difficult to secure further performances. Whenever I can, and wherever really good works are concerned, I say let's do a second performance – that way the piece begins to find a place in the repertory'.

The current focus on British music in Davis's programming reflects, at least in part, the stimulus of a new series of commercial recordings currently being made by the orchestra. A contract with WEA to make four records of British music a year has already resulted in recordings of orchestral works by Vaughan Williams (including the Sixth Symphony) and Britten, and the next project will focus on Elgar (including the First Symphony and the 'Enigma' Variations). Vaughan Williams's symphonies have only recently begun to fascinate Davis, but – to use his words – he has been passionately addicted to Elgar for most of his life. The first major work he got to know was none other than *The Dream of Gerontius*, with which he will open this year's Prom season. 'One of the first records I ever bought in my teens was Sir Malcolm Sargent's recording of *The Dream*. I absolutely adore it. It's one of those truly spiritual, visionary pieces that will change you when you hear it – and it's always a great favourite at the Proms.' He sees it as a very original work, more a dramatic cantata than a true oratorio, while Mendelssohn's *Elijah*, his second Proms collaboration with the BBC Symphony Orchestra this season (Prom 19), he describes as 'the apotheosis of the traditional nineteenth-century oratorio', although he again approaches it as a 'dramatic rather than devotional' work.

Davis believes it is part of the orchestra's role to promote British music abroad, and works by Elgar, Britten, Tippett and other living British composers feature regularly on their foreign tours, which have recently taken them as far afield as Japan. The British emphasis of their appearances at the Proms, however, is balanced by performances of Ravel's *Daphnis and Chloë* (Prom 58) and Nielsen's Fifth Symphony (Prom 63) – a work he has also recorded with the orchestra for Virgin Classics. Even the first half of the Last Night – which Davis conducts this season for the third time – has a strong non-British element, including Dame Gwyneth Jones singing Brünnhilde's Immolation Scene from *Götterdämmerung*. This unusual item came about when Dame Gwyneth confided to BBC Radio 3's Controller, John Drummond, that her great wish was to sing at the Last Night of the Proms. Both he and Davis were absolutely delighted, and did not hesitate to include in the programme the Wagner for which she is so renowned.

For Davis – and for most other people, too – the Last Night is fun, a 'uniquely festive' way to end the vast season of concerts that comprise the Proms: 'The traditional items in the Last Night have a quintessential Britishness that has nothing to do with jingoism, but which nonetheless stirs the emotions'. His personal sense of fun and the geniality and enthusiasm that characterise his approach to music-making were much in evidence last season, and are always to the fore in his relationship with the players of the BBC Symphony Orchestra: 'I'm the sort of conductor who likes to work with an orchestra in a friendly way, by persuasion rather than intimidation. I believe we're all there for the same purpose – to do the best we can – and, well, they're a wonderful bunch of people!'

Andrew Davis conducting the 1990 Last Night of the Proms

Below *The BBC Symphony Orchestra with Andrew Davis in the Hitomi Memorial Hall, Tokyo, May 1990*

A few classics you won't find at HMV.

"Grieg? I'll need his surname as well."

———◇———

"Do you know the name of it? I mean Beethoven's 5th isn't much to go on."

———◇———

"Macbeth? I think you should try the book shop round the corner."

———◇———

150 OXFORD STREET

CLASSICAL DEPT ADJACENT

WHAT YOU WILL FIND IS THE ENTIRE BRITISH CATALOGUE AND ASSISTANTS
WHO ARE ALL TRAINED MUSICIANS.

YOU CAN ORDER ANY RECORDING USING HMV'S PHONE LINE SERVICE ON 071 631 3423

SHOP OPENING HOURS 9.30 – 7.00 MONDAY – SATURDAY. 9.30 – 8.00 THURSDAY

NORTHERN LIGHTS

Gerald Larner *recounts the progress of the*
BBC Philharmonic

Edward Downes conducting the BBC
Philharmonic in January 1990

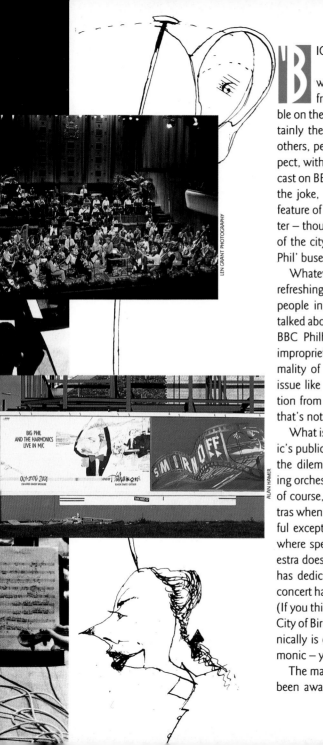

'B IG PHIL AND THE HARMONICS are in Town!' I'm not sure how the BBC Philharmonic would react if they were to hear that slogan from the floor of the Albert Hall as they assemble on the platform for one of their Proms this year. Certainly they would recognise it – some with pleasure, others, perhaps, with embarrassment, but most, I suspect, with a wry smile. As for listeners to the live broadcast on BBC Radio 3, only a minority would understand the joke, since the publicity campaign which made a feature of the slogan was restricted largely to Manchester – though in no small way and, considering the size of the city-centre posters and the ubiquity of the 'Big Phil' buses, with no small impact.

Whatever the success of the campaign in terms of refreshing the image of the orchestra and getting more people into its public concerts, it certainly got itself talked about. Indeed, there has been more discussion of BBC Philharmonic publicity, about the propriety (or impropriety) of its cheerful style, and the blotty informality of David Hughes's graphics, than of a serious issue like the impending transfer of the musical direction from Edward Downes to Yan Pascal Tortelier. But that's not the only reason why I mention it here.

What is really interesting about the BBC Philharmonic's publicity campaign is that it is a vivid illustration of the dilemma confronting just about every broadcasting orchestra. Conditions vary from country to country, of course, and none of this applies to the BBC orchestras when they come to the Proms, which are a wonderful exception to a somewhat melancholy rule: except where special conditions prevail, a broadcasting orchestra does not have the box-office appeal of one which has dedicated itself to developing a star image in the concert hall and – above all – in commercial recordings. (If you think about the recently acquired glamour of the City of Birmingham Symphony Orchestra – which technically is on much the same level as the BBC Philharmonic – you will see what I mean.)

The management of the BBC Philharmonic has long been aware of this, of course, and the orchestra has

Rehearsing with Sir Georg Solti in the Free Trade Hall, June 1990

Rehearsing with Sir Michael Tippett at the Lichfield Festival, July 1990

Far right The BBC Northern Orchestra with its conductor Charles Groves at the Pavilion Gardens, Buxton, on 20 October 1946

been giving regular seasons of subscription concerts in Manchester for eighteen years now. But all those concerts have been broadcast, which means that the programmes have had to be shaped to fit into Radio 3's grand design. On every occasion consideration has had to be given not just to maximising the paying audience but also to performing the duties of a major unit within a highly responsible national network.

Last season, for example, the Philharmonic offered its subscribers symphonies by Paul Creston and David Diamond and concertos by George Lloyd and George Nicholson – works which clearly deserved an airing but which don't have the fashionable appeal of, say, the John Adams or Michael Torke or Mark-Anthony Turnage items which a concert-hall orchestra might have chosen from equivalent areas of the repertoire.

If the BBC Symphony Orchestra has to some extent the same problem, it has also had a more coherent strategy in the promotion of contemporary music and a bigger share of the more newsworthy first performances. The Symphony Orchestra has always been at the centre of BBC musical thinking, which has been purposeful and positive on its behalf ever since it was set up – just like that – with an establishment of 114 musicians and

a permanent conductor in 1930. The Philharmonic, on the other hand, developed in a piecemeal and comparatively casual way in the first few decades after its emergence as the BBC Northern Orchestra (from the still more humble Northern Studio Orchestra) in 1934. It then had thirty or so players, which it shared with the Hallé (continuing to do so until 1943), and no permanent conductor until 1944, when a very young Charles Groves was appointed to the post. It was only in 1967, when the establishment was increased to 70 players, that the BBC Northern Orchestra was dignified by the augmentation of its name to the BBC Northern Symphony Orchestra.

When it became the BBC Philharmonic Orchestra in 1982, there was some feeling in the North that it ought to have retained the same kind of pride in its regional identity as do the BBC Scottish and BBC Welsh Symphony orchestras in their national titles. My own feeling was quite different, first of all because regional and national are not the same thing, and also because while there was both a BBC Symphony Orchestra and a BBC Northern Symphony Orchestra, one of them inevitably looked provincial. Moreover, with the new name there came an additional 19 full-time players, making 89 in all, and an at least implicit recognition of the quality of the ensemble and of its role in British musical life.

So how did the BBC Northern – once a not very enthusiastic studio band, reputedly liable to give con-

The woodwind section of the BBC Northern Orchestra, July 1962

A Pre-Proms Party?

A Midsummer COSTUME Party?

A PIRATE PARTY – FROM SCRATCH

in support of the Royal Marsden Hospital Cancer Appeal

Royal Albert Hall, Friday, 12 July 1991 at 7.30 p.m.

(Chief Executive: Patrick Deuchar)

The Tuesday Partnership and The Royal Marsden Hospital Cancer Appeal,
present in association with Midsummer Opera

THE PIRATES OF PENZANCE

Conducted by: Bramwell Tovey

(Pirate costume is optional but Come and Join In!)

Promenaders, Pirates, Policemen, Major Generals' Daughters, Music Lovers
and Singers everywhere are all welcome to join the chorus!

Bookings to:

The Tuesday Partnership
P.O. Box 323
London W4 3TY

To: "BOOKINGS",
The Tuesday Partnership
P.O. Box 323, London W4 3TY

THE PIRATES OF PENZANCE

Name ....

Address ....

....

....

....

Telephone ....

SEATS AT £12.00			
Sopr	Alto	Tenor	Bass
£12.00	BOX SEATS AT £15.00		
Audience	With Singers	Audience only	

Enter number of seats for each category above

(If you prefer EXCLUSIVE use of a BOX, the total therein should be 5, 8, or 12)

My payment, made out to

The Tuesday Partnership

totals £.................... for .... seats.

I wish part completion of this order if some seats are unavailable.
(DELETE IF NOT APPLICABLE)

★★ PLEASE send a stamped addressed envelope ★★

Downes and the orchestra in Munich

ductors who were not tough enough to deal with some of its more hard-boiled representatives a bad time – become the youthful ensemble which the BBC Philharmonic is today, with its pleasingly flexible string section and its fresh overall sound?

Thirty years ago the BBC Northern worked mainly in cramped and discouragingly makeshift conditions in the Milton Hall in Deansgate, and gave weekly midday concerts – broadcast live, admission free – in the Town Hall, where the Pre-Raphaelite murals are magnificent but the acoustics appalling. Even in these circumstances – thanks partly to George Hurst, who was Principal Conductor in the 1960s – the orchestra developed a well-balanced sound and a secure ensemble.

The major step forward was taken in 1980, when Studio 7 opened in New Broadcasting House in Manchester, making working conditions infinitely better for players and technicians alike. There are still limitations on space: Studio 7 could not be made into a full-size concert hall. But there is room for a small audience and, more importantly, for a big sound. It is a very high room, so capacious in at least this dimension that it doesn't cramp the orchestra's style in any way, and acoustically so even-tempered that it doesn't upset the balance or distort the textures. It is a place where an orchestra can develop rather than merely survive.

'Phil's Multi-Coloured Music Machine' – the BBC Philharmonic's Family Concerts (April 1990)

The other essentials were to involve the orchestra in foreign touring (which has become an increasingly important element in its activities in recent years) and to make sure that it gave more public concerts in the city in which it is based – not just to a casual audience who might drift into Manchester Town Hall or Salford University or the Royal Northern College of Music for free entertainment in their lunch-break, but to a paying public dedicating an evening and expecting its money's worth in a proper concert hall.

The only proper concert hall in Manchester – with bandroom facilities and seats for as many as 2,000 people – is, of course, the Free Trade Hall. It is not a hall which is universally liked, but in 1973 – when the BBC Northern Symphony Orchestra gave its first season of Master Concerts with a newly appointed musical director – its shortcomings were not as obvious as they have since become.

If the hall was less than ideal, however, the conductor was just right. Raymond Leppard was recognised everywhere as a brilliant musician. He was also a gifted communicator, and clearly not one who would be satisfied with a low-profile life in the studio. Indeed, when he took up his appointment with the BBC he was known mainly as a conductor of Baroque and early Classical music, and was ambitious to prove himself in a wider repertoire – which he duly did.

When Leppard left Manchester for America in 1980

Studio 7 as seen from the Control Room

Nothing's quite as good as Quad
(except a season ticket).

QUAD

For the closest approach
to the original sound

For the name and address of your nearest Quad authorised High Fidelity dealer, write to
Ross Walker at Quad Electroacoustics Ltd., Huntingdon PE18 7DB. Telephone (0480) 52561

City of Westminster

Wigmore Hall 90th Anniversary Concerts

(The Wigmore Hall opened with two inaugural concerts on 31 May and 1 June 1901)

wigmore

Friday
31 May
7.30pm
STEVEN ISSERLIS cello / **NIKOLAI DEMIDENKO** piano / **OLLI**
MUSTONEN piano / **PASCAL ROGÉ** piano / **SARAH WALKER**
mezzo soprano and **ROGER VIGNOLES** piano
Music composed in 1901
Rakhmaninov: Cello Sonata in G minor op 19
Schoenberg: Cabaret Songs
Sibelius: Malinconia for cello and piano op 20
Piano solos by **Grieg, Rakhmaninov, Janáček, Debussy, Ravel** etc.

Saturday
1 June
7.30pm
BRIGITTE FASSBAENDER mezzo soprano
GRAHAM JOHNSON piano
Songs by Schubert

Sunday
2 June
7pm
THE ENGLISH CONCERT
TREVOR PINNOCK director, harpsichord
NANCY ARGENTA soprano
MARK BENNETT trumpet
Torelli: Sinfonia in D G8 for trumpet and strings
Geminiani/Corelli: Concerto Grosso in C
Bach: Harpsichord Concerto in D minor BWV1052
Wassanaer: Concerto Armonico no 4 in G
Bach: Cantata 51 *Jauchzet Gott in allen Landen*

Tuesday
4 June
7.30 pm
MIECZYSLAW HORSZOWSKI piano
The legendary Mieczyslaw Horszowski will be 99 in June - he
has the longest international career in Western music.

Wednesday
5 June
7.30pm
BARBARA BONNEY soprano
GEOFFREY PARSONS piano
Songs by **Mendelssohn, Hugo Wolf, Grieg, Zemlinsky, Berg**
and **Richard Strauss**

Friday
7 June
7.30pm
BEAUX ARTS TRIO
Schubert: Trio in B flat D898
Piano Trios by **Haydn** and **Zemlinsky**

Saturday
8 June
7.30pm
THE SONGMAKERS' ALMANAC
John Mark Ainsley tenor / **Patricia Rozario** soprano
Richard Jackson baritone / **Sarah Walker** mezzo soprano
Graham Johnson piano
A programme based on six months at the Wigmore Hall in 1901,
and on events in that year.

Sunday
9 June
7pm
THE NASH ENSEMBLE
WOLFGANG HOLZMAIR baritone
Beethoven: Folk Songs
Schumann: Piano Quartet in E flat op 47
Weber: Flute Trio in G minor op 63
Mahler: Songs of a Wayfarer (arr. Schoenberg)

Saturday
15 June
7.30pm
FELICITY LOTT soprano
ANN MURRAY mezzo soprano
GRAHAM JOHNSON piano
Duets and songs by **Purcell, Mendelssohn, Rossini, Brahms,**
Gounod, Saint-Saëns and **Fauré**

Thursday
20 June
7.30pm
OLAF BAER baritone
GEOFFREY PARSONS piano
Schumann: Dichterliebe op 48; Liederkreis op 39

Wednesday
26 June
7.30pm
FRANÇOISE POLLET soprano
JEAN-MARC LUISADA piano
First London appearance of the outstanding new French soprano.
Berlioz: Les Nuits d'Eté; Songs by **Poulenc, Schumann,**
Britten etc.

Saturday
29 June
7.30pm
MARGARET PRICE soprano
GRAHAM JOHNSON piano

Sunday
30 June
7pm
ELLY AMELING soprano
RUDOLF JANSEN piano
Favourites of Fifteen Years at the Wigmore Hall
Songs by **Haydn, Mozart, Schubert, Schumann, Brahms,**
Hugo Wolf, Richard Strauss, Fauré, Debussy, Ravel, Poulenc,
Duparc - and many others!

Monday
1 July
7.30pm
PETER SCHREIER tenor
ANDRAS SCHIFF piano
Schubert Programme: Rellstab and Heine Lieder from
Schwanengesang; 9 Goethe Lieder

wigmore

After the Concert on 1 July, the Wigmore Hall will close for the installation of
additional facilities and will re-open with a Gala Concert on 10 October 1992

Booking Information
Brochure, booking details and tickets from:
Wigmore Hall Box Office, 36 Wigmore Street, London W1H 9DF
Tel: 071-935 2141. All major credit cards accepted.

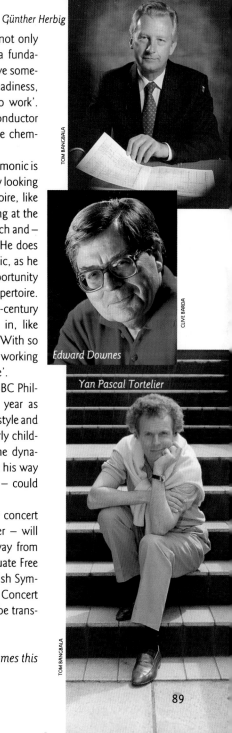

he was succeeded by the BBC Philharmonic's present Principal Conductor. The arrival of Edward Downes – less colourful a personality than Leppard, perhaps, but certainly no less inspired or accomplished a musician – coincided with the appointment of Günther Herbig as Chief Guest Conductor. It was an exceptionally useful combination – Downes bringing to the orchestra an extraordinarily wide range of interests and authority, but making a particular speciality of Russian and British music, Herbig giving it the benefit of his experience in the central-European repertoire and above all in Bruckner.

Downes and Herbig – and from 1985 to 1989 Downes and Bernhard Klee – made the orchestra a secure and stable ensemble, strong enough to carry the weight of the great Romantic symphonies, but stylish in the classics, too, and highly sophisticated in the modern repertoire. As Sir Peter Maxwell Davies has said – remembering with particular gratitude the first performance and the splendid recording of his Third Symphony, which was commissioned to celebrate the orchestra's 50th birthday in 1984 – no-one has done more for new orchestral music than Ted Downes.

In 1992, however, after 12 years in the post – which is a long time for any conductor to stay with any orchestra these days – Downes will be leaving the BBC Philharmonic to be succeeded by Yan Pascal Tortelier. This, of course, is a far more important issue for the BBC Philharmonic than the much-debated 'Big Phil' style of publicity. But the two are not wholly unrelated. If the orchestra is looking for a new public, it can only be helpful that its Principal Conductor is so obviously endowed with the Tortelier family personality – good looks, Gallic charm, and unmistakable sincerity. These qualities are undoubtedly among those which have made Tortelier so successful with Belfast audiences, as Principal Conductor of the Ulster Orchestra, and they will surely prove no less effective in Manchester.

Moreover, to get to the fundamental point, he will be bringing to the BBC Philharmonic impeccable musical breeding, inherited from his late and much-loved cellist father, and they in return will be giving him not only what he finds in most British orchestras – 'a fundamental ability to play as an ensemble, to achieve something together' – but also 'an extraordinary readiness, an ability to respond, a 200% willingness to work'. Clearly, that indefinable quality, the blend of conductor and orchestra personality – what he calls 'the chemistry' – is right.

A quality he values highly in the BBC Philharmonic is its 'clear and precise' sound. 'So I'm particularly looking forward to the big modern symphonic repertoire, like the Bertók Concerto for Orchestra we are doing at the Proms this year, the symphonies of Shostakovich and – this is a tribute to Ted Downes – Prokofiev.' He does not intend to make a speciality of French music, as he has done in Belfast, but welcomes the opportunity offered by the BBC to embrace a much wider repertoire. 'It will be very interesting to explore twentieth-century British music ... and other things I believe in, like Honegger, Roussel, Dutilleux and Hindemith. With so much repertoire to develop and experience, working with this orchestra will open new doors for me'.

Interestingly, Tortelier's first year with the BBC Philharmonic will coincide with En Shao's last year as Associate Conductor. That combination – the style and taste of a French conductor nurtured since early childhood in the best European traditions, and the dynamism of a Chinese conductor who has fought his way into the profession against impossible odds – could prove irresistible.

By 1993 Manchester should have its new concert hall which – unless it is a complete disaster – will restore the audience at present dwindling away from orchestral concerts in the now plainly inadequate Free Trade Hall. If the experience of the BBC Scottish Symphony Orchestra in the new Glasgow Royal Concert Hall is anything to go by, the situation could be transformed overnight.

For details of the BBC Philharmonic's programmes this season, see Proms 8, 9, 41 and 42

COLCHESTER INSTITUTE

SCHOOL OF MUSIC

Head W Tamblyn BA, A Cert.CM., F.R.S.A.
The School of Music is a community of musicians with over 250 students, 17 full-time and 60 part-time staff, including many teachers with a national reputation. There are orchestras, choirs and other ensembles. The courses are a valuable preparation for careers in performance, teaching or administration.

B.A.(C.N.A.A.) Honours Degree

Major options from the second year include:
PERFORMANCE, STYLISTIC AND FREE COMPOSITION, DISSERTATION, CHRISTIAN LITURGICAL MUSIC AND CONDUCTING.

G.MUS.(C.N.A.A.) Graduate Diploma

Two pathways from the second year (Performance and Vocational). Options include:
SCHOOL BASED STUDIES, MUSIC FOR PEOPLE WITH SPECIAL NEEDS, BUSINESS STUDIES FOR MUSICIANS, MUSIC AND TECHNOLOGY, PERFORMANCE.

FOUNDATION DIPLOMA

Preparation for double 'A' level in Music, ABRSM exams other 'A' levels, and entrance to conservatories.

ONE YEAR COURSES Self-funding

A Preliminary Certificate (based on the Foundation Course) and an Advanced Certificate (based on the G.Mus course) are available for those from non-EEC countries who are prepared to pay full-cost.

Details of the Institute, the School of Music and the Courses are available on request (by telephone or letter)
Colchester Institute, Sheepen Road, Colchester, Essex, C03 3LL
Telephone (0206) 761660

THE 1991/92 SEASON
OPENS AUGUST 17

NEW PRODUCTIONS

THE MARRIAGE OF FIGARO
Wolfgang Amadeus Mozart

DIE FLEDERMAUS
Johann Strauss

KÖNIGSKINDER
Engelbert Humperdinck

DON CARLOS
Giuseppe Verdi

WORLD PREMIÈRE

THE BACCHAE
John Buller

REVIVALS INCLUDE:

BILLY BUDD, A MASKED BALL, XERXES, STREET SCENE, ORFEO and THE RETURN OF ULYSSES

All operas are sung in English

Mailing List **071 836 3908**

English National Opera, London Coliseum, St Martin's Lane, London WC2N 4ES

Arts Council Funded

Another classical performer

SD-Scicon plc, Centrum House, 101-103 Fleet Road, Fleet, Hampshire, GU13 8NZ. Telephone: 0252 622161.

P R O M S

Bush House, headquarters of
the BBC World Service

INTERNATIONAL

Lindsay Kemp explains how Henry Wood's aim of broadening audiences for classical music is being achieved on a global scale

OW DO YOU EXPERIENCE THE PROMS? If you live in Britain, but too far away from London to get to the Royal Albert Hall, the chances are that you tune in to Radio 3's comprehensive coverage of the season. But for those who live abroad this is not an available option; Radio 3's signal does not reach much further than the other side of the Channel. So how do people in, say, Hong Kong or Haiti get to enjoy the atmosphere of this great international festival?

One answer is by listening to the BBC's World Service. In this country the activities of this important part of the BBC are frequently overlooked; insomniacs who pick it up on Radio 4's long-wave frequency during the small hours of the morning are well aware of its quality, but for those who have never heard the World Service the name perhaps smacks of plummy voices speaking to distant, out-of-touch expatriates. They might even – though quite unjustifiably – associate its dissemination of news and current affairs through 37 different language services with the dark realms of government propaganda.

But the truth is very different; there is an estimated global audience of 120 million (a figure which does not take into account listeners in a number of countries for which research has not been possible, such as China, Cuba and Iran), and the respect which the BBC World Service commands has been demonstrated time and again by the part it continues to play in world events. On a visit in March 1990 to Bush House, the World Service's London headquarters, the Czech President, Vaclav Havel, told of his gratitude for 50 years of programmes from the BBC's Czechoslovak section, adding: 'it is very important that these broadcasts continue as part of Czechoslovakia's change to democracy'. And the previous summer, Chinese students engaged in their own desperate struggle for human

Students marching in Peking, 1989

rights in Tiananmen Square held up banners with the simple message: 'Thank you BBC'.

But the World Service isn't just news. Its English-language service offers drama, documentaries, light entertainment, sport — in fact, the same range of programmes as the national networks. Classical music, too, has an important place in the schedules, where it enjoys the support of World Service Managing Director John Tusa, himself a regular concert- and opera-goer, and last year a presenter of *Omnibus at the Proms*. Compared to Radio 3, the World Service Music Department is small — it has just three full-time producers — but it maintains a regular and varied output. This includes concerts and recitals from the major British festivals; *Music Review*, a magazine programme with a high international profile (Zubin Mehta is just one of the celebrities to have appeared in the programme who is also a regular listener); and *International Recital*, a prestigious concert series which in the past season has included contributions from artists as diverse as Michael Roll, Paco Peña and The Dufay Collective.

Things go into overdrive during the Proms, however. The World Service transmits from over half the concerts in the season, taking the first half of every Saturday-night concert and usually about 20 others — including the First and Last Nights — live, and offering a regular Sunday-afternoon recorded *From the Proms* programme throughout the season. For the World Service the Proms are simply too big an international occasion to miss. Executive Music Producer Jeremy Siepmann (a voice well-known to Radio 3 listeners in the UK as a presenter of *Mainly for Pleasure* and *Saturday Review*) comments, 'the Proms are not just concerts, they are recognised all over the world as a phenomenon. It's the atmosphere, not just the music.' And he makes the point that that phenomenon is one to which the World Service itself contributes: 'Even if you take a fairly cautious estimate of the percentage of the total World Service audience that is listening to the Proms, it's a fantastic number.' The response is enormous. Listeners write in from all over the world, enabling some kind of picture to be drawn of the type of person who tunes in. Significantly, many are people who have never set foot in this country, and may never have been to a concert, but who are captivated by the extraordinary atmosphere of the Proms. Letters come from China, India, West Africa, and almost all of them, according to Senior Music Producer Elizabeth Francis, are 'full of love'.

Like Siepmann, Francis has a good deal of experience behind the microphone. World Service producers frequently present their own programmes, and she has announced at many concerts over the years, but the Proms throw up special challenges. 'It's quite a feat', she instances, 'to describe the Albert Hall to someone who has never seen a building like it. How *do* you describe it? Then again, if it's very hot in the hall, you might be talking to an audience where it's freezing cold; or you'll have to remember not to say "this evening" or "tonight" because you might be talking to someone who's just woken up. To conjure up a picture of a packed Albert Hall for someone who's crawling out of an igloo first thing in the morning is quite a challenge!'

Quite apart from the problem of time zones, there are technical difficulties involved in broadcasting music to the world. A short-wave receiver is hardly the best piece of equipment on which to listen to classical music, and

John Tusa with Vaclav Havel

Elizabeth Francis in the control room

Below *Jeremy Siepmann (at the piano) with producer Roger Short*

Poster for Radio New Zealand's Concert Programme *featuring the* Proms *and other items from BBC Transcription's catalogue*

recording and engineering, as Quentin Fuller, BBC Transcription's Music Organiser (and before that an engineer in the department), points out: 'In the 1950s we were one of the first departments in the BBC to have tape. Then in 1962 we started to use stereo, which the BBC didn't do for general broadcasting until 1966; we even experimented with quadrophony during the 1970s'. For a long time now Transcription programmes have been issued on black vinyl, but from this year onwards CDs will be used (a fact that will no doubt please buyers in tropical countries who have sometimes had problems with warping!).

All of which serves music well. One seventh of BBC Transcription's output is devoted to classical music, with concerts being recorded all over the country. As a result, a vast treasury has been built up, including historic occasions such as William Walton conducting the world premiere of his own *Variations on a Theme of Hindemith* in 1963, the first ever performance of Rameau's opera *Les Boréades* (which took place as recently as 1975), and Leonard Bernstein's unforgettable account of Mahler's Fifth Symphony with the Vienna Philharmonic at the Proms in 1987. In 1990 alone the Proms taken by BBC Transcription ranged from Handel's *Belshazzar* to the new symphony by Poul Ruders, and customers have included broadcasting organisations from Scandinavia to the Pacific. And often the Proms find an important place in a subscribing radio station's output, drawing appreciative responses such as this, from Miles Rogers, Programme Director of Radio New Zealand's *Concert Programme*, who maintains that they 'set a standard by which we here measure ourselves and to which our own musicians can aspire'.

More than half the Prom season on the World Service, up to a third available through BBC Transcription – there must be few places in the world where you can't hear the Proms at some time or other. Henry Wood's original intention of bringing classical music to an ever wider range of audiences could hardly be realised on a grander scale.

even with satellites now making good quality FM listening possible in more parts of the world, the need to avoid too wide a dynamic range affects the choice of music broadcast. But the BBC has an answer in the form of its Transcription service (again part of the World Service), which makes programmes specifically for sale on disc to overseas broadcasting organisations. Every year it produces 350 hours of original material – including many Proms – which is then made available to radio stations worldwide. As the BBC's Head of Transcription Peter James explains, 'thousands of people who never tune in to the World Service on short-wave can hear BBC programmes on their own local radio stations, often with very much better quality'. There are buyers all over the world, from Austria to Australasia to America to the Far East, with Japan proving to be a rapidly growing market. The department contributed over £1 million to the BBC's running costs in 1989.

The need to ensure that programmes can withstand repeated listening is met by a high standard of

"BARBICAN TO PROMMERS:
CHEER UP!
THERE IS MUSICAL LIFE AFTER THE LAST NIGHT"

THE BARBICAN HALL - THE ALL SEATER CONCERT HALL. QUEUING OPTIONAL.

ALL YEAR ROUND, THE BARBICAN CENTRE OFFERS MANY OF LONDON'S BEST CONCERTS.

The facing page gives just some of our highlights for the 1991-92 season. To receive a free copy of our colourful new monthly brochure, simply complete the form below and return to the address given.

Name _____

Address _____

_____

_____ Postcode _____

Send to: *Barbican Centre Mailing List Department, FREEPOST, London EC2B 2AT (no stamp required)*

The **LONDON SYMPHONY ORCHESTRA,** still London's only resident orchestra opens the season with Principal Conductor **Michael Tilson Thomas** conducting the world première of a new work by John Tavener for clarinet and orchestra (19 September).

The LSO's season continues with a major celebration of Prokofiev's centenary, conducted by **Mstislav Rostropovich,** with soloists **Itzhak Perlman, Martha Argerich** and **Vladimir Feltsman** (3 November - 1 December). As part of the Prokofiev Festival, the **Nash Ensemble** explore his chamber music in five concerts (4-24 November).

Other Autumn season highlights include:
MOZART 200 - PART II *(28 September - 5 December)*

The **English Chamber Orchestra** continue their chronological series of Mozart concerts, culminating in a performance of the Requiem on 5 December, the 200th anniversary of Mozart's death. Artists in Part II include **Jeffrey Tate, Christoph Eschenbach, Radu Lupu, András Schiff, Mitsuko Uchida, The Takács Quartet** and **Pinchas Zukerman.**

GREAT ORCHESTRAS OF THE WORLD

This popular series continues with a Dvořák cycle from the **Czech Philharmonic** (24, 25 and 27 September), the **Suisse Romande** (29 October) and two concerts from the **Leningrad Philharmonic** (18 and 19 November)

TAKEMITSU SERIES *(10 - 13 October)*

A celebration of the music of Toru Takemitsu, including two concerts from the LSO, with **Julian Bream, Paul Crossley and Peter Serkin, the BBC Welsh Symphony under Tadaaki Otaka,** and a recital from **Julian Bream** and **Sebastian Bell,** Plus workshops, films, talks and concerts in the **Guildhall School.**

THE CHAMBER ORCHESTRA OF EUROPE

Return for their fifth residency at the Barbican, in two concerts conducted by **Franz Bruggen** (22 and 25 November)

BOOKING OPENS SATURDAY 3 AUGUST FOR THE AUTUMN CONCERTS LISTED - AT THE BOX OFFICE - 071 638 8891 (9AM - 8PM DAILY)

The LSO's residency at the Barbican is jointly funded by the Arts Council of Great Britain and the Corporation of London. The Barbican Hall programme is promoted on behalf of, and with the support of, the Corporation of London, who own, fund and manage the Barbican Centre. Managing Director: Detta O'Cathain OBE. Barbican Centre, Silk Street, London EC2Y 8DS.

CALLING THE TUNE
SINCE 1909.

Selfridges

SELFRIDGES LTD., OXFORD STREET, LONDON W1A 1AB. TELEPHONE: 071-629 1234.

The Malcolm Sargent Cancer Fund for Children
Patron: H.R.H. THE PRINCESS OF WALES

THE MALCOLM SARGENT SUMMER CONCERT

VIENNESE EVENING

Overture: Waldmeister	**Johann Strauss II**
Hark the Mountains Resound (The Seasons)	**Haydn**
Horn Concerto No. 4 in E flat major, K495	**Mozart**
Tritsch-Tratsch Polka	**Johann Strauss II**
Frei Kugeln (Free Shoot) Polka	**Johann Strauss II**
Gems of Viennese Operetta	**arr. Tausky**
Waltz: Roses from the South	**Johann Strauss II**
Violin Concerto No. 4 in D major, K218	**Mozart**
Fata-Morgana – Polka-Mazur	**Johann Strauss II**
Furioso Polka	**Johann Strauss II**
Waltz: The Blue Danube	**Johann Strauss II**

IDA HAENDEL *violin*   **BARRY TUCKWELL** *horn*

MALCOLM SARGENT FESTIVAL CHOIR
THE ROYAL PHILHARMONIC POPS

VILEM TAUSKY *conductor*

ROYAL ALBERT HALL

Sunday 15 September 1991 at 7.30pm

*Tickets: Credit Card & Telephone Bookings 071-589 8212 and Agents
from 8 May (postal applications) and 10 June (personal applications)
and after 14 August, 14 Abingdon Road, London W8 6AF. Tel: 071-937 4547*

*Grand Tier: £15.00   Loggia: £12.00   Stalls: £11.00
Second Tier: £9.00   Front Arena: £8.50   Back Arena: £7.50
Balcony: £5.00   Balcony (restricted view): £2.00*

All available in advance

PLEASE

send a stamped and
addressed envelope to

**The Malcolm Sargent
Cancer Fund**

14 Abingdon Road
London W8 6AF

for

Full colour brochure of
the 1991 Christmas cards
(six designs in packs of
6 cards/envelopes)

and

Details of the 1992 Calendar
and Diary

Requests for further
information about the Fund's
work and/or Deed of
Covenant forms and donations
(which will be gratefully
acknowledged) may be sent to
the address above.

Performers, writers and composers from what was the Eastern bloc make a significant contribution to this year's Proms. Gerard McBurney talks to some of them, and offers timely reflections on continuing change in the East and its potential significance for music

A T THE END OF 1988 a Russian pianist of great talent arrived in London. He'd last been to the West nearly twenty years before. After that, he'd never been allowed to travel abroad. His life from then on had been hedged around with more and more restrictions. He'd lost his job and his home. He'd had no piano on which to work. For most of the past ten years he'd lived in one room with two others in a communal flat of great squalor. I know; I saw him there.

One of the first things he did in London was to ring an old friend now living in Europe: Gidon Kremer. Kremer sounded delighted and enthusiastic that my friend was now here too. 'So', he exclaimed, 'we lived to see the day!'

What day is that? At the beginning of this year, there were tanks in the streets of Vilnius and in Riga the barricades were ready. There was defiance in Moldavia and Estonia, plotting in the Caucasus, there were pogroms in the cities of Central Asia and food-shortages everywhere. This is what *The Sunday Times* recently called 'the new freedom in the Soviet Union'. As for Eastern Europe, rumours abound of rigged elections, Communists by any other name and nationalist plots. Senior ministers in one of the most warmly welcomed of the new régimes are said to devote their cabinet meetings to drinking alcohol. Perhaps they've nothing better to do.

The joy that greeted *glasnost* and *perestroika*, the fall of the Wall and the end of Ceaucescu, was distinctly understandable; but even then most of us must have wondered how unsure was what's to come. Now we know. And even supposing the trumpeted ideal, even supposing that vast areas of people trapped in poverty and unabsolved resentment were really able to imagine the famous 'market' or 'democracy', what then?

The artists who lived under the various totalitarian governments in Eastern Europe and beyond, were, whatever their hatred of those who oppressed them, sustained by those same oppressors in a strange symbiosis. This was, of course, in part the oppressor's intention. If you weren't actually one of those who were repressed, then your particular union of writers, composers, artists, or whatever, while interfering in your private artistic decisions, could also provide material conditions that made those decisions possible. These could include anything from flat and food to almost free accommodation (as Western artists noted enviously) in 'Houses of Creation', or villages, where you could, if you were lucky, stay whole months and work.

Much the same went for performers. The various organisations arranging performers' work exerted a dispiriting control over repertoire and opportunity. But they, too, could provide relative advantages. And above all, like the 'creative' unions, they could woo your loyalty by subterfuge, by freeing you of some of the

Shostakovich making his opening address at the Fourth Congress of Soviet Composers: left to right *Leonid Brezhnev, Alexey Kosygin, Shostakovich, Tikhon Khrennikov (leader of the Soviet Composers' Union)*

CHANGE OR DECAY?

Fireworks over the Brandenburg Gate:
the re-unification of Germany, 3 October 1990

Irina Ratushinskaya

Witold Lutoslawski

responsibilities — financial and practical, mundane and time-consuming — which hung around the necks of everyone else.

But there's a deeper sense in which these artists in the East were involved in the very régimes that they hated (or perhaps loved). For those régimes so often gave the artists their very theme, as well as a whole surrounding emotional scaffolding of symbol and implication. In novel after play after symphony after painting from what was the Communist Bloc, we find the clarity of the message as well as the message itself rooted in an awareness of the political conditions under which the work was both made and intended to be experienced by others.

Of course you can retort that this is a condition of art anyway. To say that an artist's work depends on those in power is perhaps only to say that it depends on the society in which the artist lives. Imagine Milton without Cromwell or Elgar without Empire. Yes, but the condition in recent years in Eastern Europe was different and distinct, if only because of the curious simplicity of the demonology and the starkness of its symbolism. Sir Harrison Birtwistle might write a piece in which every note is a personal assault on the Conservative Party. But we are unlikely to be touched in the same way that a Russian audience five years ago would have been touched by the religious ending to Sofia Gubaidulina's mighty violin concerto, *Offertorium*.

So what happens when this relationship between the artist and the state simply, or complicatedly, crumbles away? What symbols do you, as an artist, use now to make yourself clear? Or, if you are a performer, what do you perform when the 'dissident art' with which you once daringly thrilled your audience turns out to be just plain old 'modern art' which nobody wants? And how do you cope when the head of the Composers' Union, who'd insisted you played his ghastly *Hymn to Lenin*, is replaced by an agent and an audience who insist you only do the standard repertoire? And they get their way by paying you more, rather than by threatening you? Or what happens when nobody wants to pay you to play

anything — however talented you might be — because there are already too many people in the same place with the same instrument, or people are just spending their money on different things this year? Is not your last state worse than your first?

Irina Ratushinskaya is an artist whose fame in the West began out of her sufferings in the East, sufferings vividly reflected in the five of her poems chosen by Brian Elias for his orchestral song-cycle. But she is quick to reject the idea of hankering for the security of a more brutal past:

'In the first place I think the less politics are connected with art and music the better. The only thing artists needed before was to be left alone. And that has happened, not because politicians have suddenly become interested in art, but because they now have too many other things to think about — like striking miners, a collapsing economy and everything else ...'

In a recent newspaper interview Witold Lutoslawski went further. He described how he had always felt the need to keep his music concentrated on himself. Earlier this had been a question not only of resisting the demands of those in authority but also of those fighting against them. His music had had to be kept free of either side. Now his struggle is to keep it free of yet other kinds of interference. The noise of commerce, for instance. In Poland, he said, this is literally the noise of muzak, invading every public place. It seems that silence is what people are afraid of now.

But for those unlike Lutoslawski, who have not his steely determination to remain aloof from what other people want him to say, the new and unfamiliar pressures must often seem difficult. Lothar Zagrosek is a Westerner who has recently taken on responsibility for a whole community that until now was 'in the East', the Opera in Leipzig. He is struck by the psychology of those working there whose future is now in his hands:

'Before, they lived in a closed paradise ... not, of course, a paradise in the Western sense, but in the

A REAL SENSE OF ACHIEVEMENT

Royal Academy of Music
Royal College of Music
Royal Northern College of Music
Royal Scottish Academy
of Music and Drama

ASSOCIATED BOARD
OF THE ROYAL SCHOOLS OF MUSIC

The Associated Board of the
Royal Schools of Music
14 Bedford Square
London WC1B 3JG

Telephone 071-636 5400/4478
Fax 071-436 4520

Registered as Charity No. 292182

GRADED MUSIC EXAMINATIONS

Lothar Zagrosek conducting in Leipzig

Libor Pešek in Prague

sense that everything around them was *sure*, their job, their pension ... Now they have freedom, but no possibility to live. I see that they are very anxious and a bit frightened. Nothing has its place for them anymore, and this leads them into very aggressive feelings. The world of big competition is very difficult, and those who have stayed in Eastern Europe feel very provincial.'

Zagrosek himself supposes that his role in the situation is to help by recognising other people's feelings and by offering practical ways to cope:

'I am showing people how to take responsibility for themselves, how to learn to trust democratic culture. They must learn that *that* is the basis of real creativity, where there are no rules and each must think for himself or herself. The biggest problem I have in the Leipzig Opera is to show them the way to *real true* expression.'

The Czech conductor Libor Pešek is even blunter. He recently commented:

'In the end money will always be found somehow. Here in Britain one simply employs a different way of going round the benefactors ... What matters is quality – and under the old régime, quality wasn't always there. This is why I think that Czech art and Czech music will experience a revival. A few people will fall by the wayside, but the majority of those who do produce quality will soon realise that the

new type of existence is not only possible but that it is also better.'

Inevitably, one of the effects of the breaking-up of the old order is a big migration westwards. Many musicians are being swept towards us in this flood. Some of these are already famous, world-class soloists who simply wish to lead their international careers themselves. These are the ones we hear about. Then there are the bands. No less than three of the most famous chamber orchestras in the Soviet Union – Liana Isakadze's Georgian Chamber Orchestra, Vladimir Spivakov's Moscow Virtuosi and now Yuri Bashmet's Moscow Soloists – have all found permanent homes in Western Europe. And they have all brought their families with them. And there are, as well, many tens of thousands of ordinary musicians of different backgrounds and ages, finding their way by legal and illegal means and for a variety of reasons.

Partly this migration is in search of a better life, of a richer and (it is fondly hoped) a more appreciative audience. Over and again in recent months I have heard new arrivals say: 'They don't need musicians back home, they need businessmen/engineers/farmers/technologists. What is there for me to do back there?' It is not surprising that most Eastern European musicians report a drop in audience attendance.

Partly – especially in the case of the Soviet Union – a musician's need to move is a result of the disgusting and egregious resurgence of anti-Semitism. Great num-

Former times: the First All-Union Congress of Soviet Composers, Moscow, 19 April 1948

bers of Jewish artists are leaving for the understandable reason that they wish their families to remain alive.

But there's perhaps another reason, one on which Lothar Zagrosek put his finger when he spoke of people feeling 'provincial'. In the old days, when almost no-one could travel, a curious effect was produced. Moscow provides an obvious example. Twenty years ago that city had one of the richest communities of performing musicians in the world, a community fed by the imagined heritage of Rubinstein, Rakhmaninov and other masters of a former age. It was a community with a dense network of contacts and relationships within itself – especially between composers and performers and between practitioners of the different arts. But at the same time it had almost no regular or open contact with other artistic communities in the rest of the world. Foreign artists rarely came to play, their recordings and writings were hard to get hold of. Except for the very grand and the very daring (like Gennady Rozhdestvensky or Mstislav Rostropovich), those Soviet artists who were sent abroad had almost no contact with their colleagues in the countries they visited.

What flourishes in such a condition of isolation is the concentration of talent, the building of a self-regarding world, feeding off itself and dependent on its own resources. It's a situation that can produce the most wonderful music-making. But it is also, paradoxically, dependent on a doubting curiosity about the unknown world outside. You can't keep reassuring yourself that you don't need other people, without at the same time

needing them; you need proof that you are right. So when your isolation begins to grow less, your curiosity becomes the greater. And in the end you have to travel to the West to find out for yourself. And when you get there you find that the community to which you've come is not the same as the one you left. Indeed, it's not really a community in the same sense. It is incomprehensibly larger and quite without the close organic ties and links you'd been used to. No matter how confident you may be in the superiority of your playing, you cannot be at all sure that anybody here wants to hear you.

Those artists who are already long-established in the West see this situation from several points of view. Vladimir Ashkenazy, for example, is insistent that the opportunity for artists in the East to travel to the West can bring nothing but good, that new openness will bring new richness and the possibility of development. The pianist Dmitri Alexeev, on the other hand, is more ambivalent. Unlike Ashkenazy, he has never moved completely to the West. Although he has spent nearly twenty years travelling and playing here, he has remained resident in the USSR as well as elsewhere in Eastern Europe. He is adamant that the results of the new freedom of movement could be harder to understand than we might think.

'For the composers the effect of the political changes on music has brought nothing but good. The 'avant-garde' composers, like Schnittke,

Dmitri Alexeev

Vladimir Ashkenazy
in Moscow

Coca-Cola

The Opening Movement

You Can't Beat The Feeling!

'Coca-Cola' and 'Coke' are registered trade marks which
identify the same product of The Coca-Cola Company.

Gubaidulina and so on, were virtually unknown before, and now they are performed all over the world. And of course the lives of performers have been changed for the good, too, simply in that they can now decide their own careers. They can travel where they want, accept the engagements they want, live where they want and make their own contracts.'

For Alexeev this is not the question. The question comes when you wonder what it is that makes these artists from the Eastern Bloc so particularly themselves: what it is, in fact, that makes us want to listen to them. Does their distinctive quality so depend on where they came from that it will now be lost? How will the distinctive traditions of Prague or Moscow (or Leipzig or Odessa) survive the levelling that must now take place, let alone the loss of half the players or their removal into other countries?

Dmitri Alexeev is cautious:

'How the political changes will really change musicians – inwardly change the way they actually play – won't be known for a long time. For the moment, at any rate, they will probably stay the same. And maybe those performers who are already established will never really change. Contact with the outside world, with outside traditions and ways of thinking, has maybe come too late to affect them. They will already have been formed by the world in which they grew up. But for the younger players, for those who have not yet appeared, things will certainly be different. These are the ones that will have to make sense of the new situation. And in ways that we will only understand in ten or twenty years time.'

Alexeev ends on a note of diplomatic optimism:

'Perhaps then we will hear some kind of new synthesis, a synthesis of the different traditions ...'

Interestingly, Libor Pešek also speaks in this context of the possibility of synthesis. He is even enthusiastic about his own plans in this respect:

'In Czechoslovakia, *spiccato* is played in a different way, whereas here it is somewhat broader; I like that very much. But I would like to introduce a kind of Slavonic rhythmisation, where the *staccato* is sustained a little, which has the effect of bringing some sparkle to playing.'

The idea of synthesis, with its threat of the loss of distinct identity, can often seem a less than exciting prospect. But in the real world part of us must hope that these artists are right to look forward to such things. At least as far as the Soviet Union goes, it seems disagreeably possible just now that the opposite of synthesis may happen. The younger generation of musicians may find themselves, like their predecessors in 1917, suddenly cut off, shut inside a closed world from which the older generation of artists will have fled. If that happens, it will be hard once again to pick up the threads of tradition. And we will all be the losers.

Sofia Gubaidulina

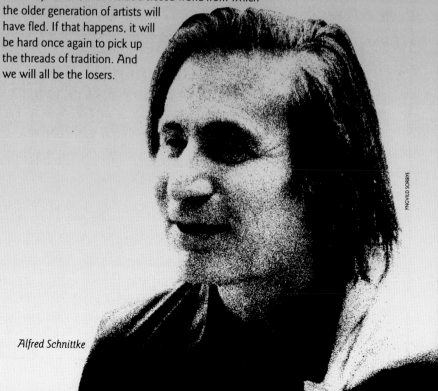

Alfred Schnittke

Ring & Brymer

AT THE

ROYAL ALBERT HALL

Ring & BRYMER invite you to enjoy first class cuisine on the occasion of the 1991 Proms Concerts and offer you a range of alternatives designed to suit your particular preferences and of course the style of the occasion.
Telephone 01-589-8900/7976

ELGAR ROOM RESTAURANT
on the Balcony Level (enter by door 8).
This beautifully decorated room offers a full waiter service restaurant with a selection of dishes every day.

Open daily from 5.15 p.m. Table reservation possible.

PRINCE CONSORT ROOM
on the first floor level (enter by doors 13/14).
This self service buffet is open for every show offering a hot roast meal, salads and pastries.

Open daily 45 minutes prior to each show.

BROTHER INTERNATIONAL EUROPE LTD · BROTHER HOUSE · 1 TAME STREET AUDENSHAW · MANCHESTER M34 5JE
MICROWAVES · TYPEWRITERS · KNITTING MACHINES · COMPUTERS · COMPUTER PRINTERS
COLOUR COPIERS · INDUSTRIAL AND DOMESTIC SEWING MACHINES · FACSIMILES

The best in music

BBC RADIO THREE 3

Music Weekly with Peter Paul Nash

Soundings with Michael Oliver

Opera News with James Naughtie

Saturday Review with Richard Osborne

and much more...

Tuning Up with Chris de Souza

Third Opinion with Christopher Cook

*f**m** stereo 90.2-92.4*

Science & Arts Documentaries

Philosophy & Politics

Drama Now

Poet of the Month

Table Talk

Sunday Play

Third Ear

INDEX OF WORKS

** First performance at a Henry
Wood Promenade Concert*

David Bedford

Brian Elias

PABLO KELLER

'PERFORMANCE IN THE ROUND'

ATH-611

ATH-609

Just as the circle is an essential ingredient of the Royal Albert Hall, Audio Technica's latest 600 Series headphones maximise it's potential for sound reproduction. Using large diameter yet ultra thin diaphragms, A-T's engineers cleverly combine them with an especially large internal earspace cavity and a high sensitivity Samarium Cobalt magnet system to produce a superb level of sound quality at a highly affordable price. They're also designed for comfort ... hour upon hour if the mood takes you ... and feature infinitely adjustable headbands and 'soft feel' earpads.

A leading hi-fi magazine recently wrote *'the 609 itself is a fine budget headphone for the audiophile, punchy, dynamic and enjoyable'* - 'at anything below full wick the 610's were an excellent headphone, comfortable to wear, musically coherent ...' - 'open, crystal clear and with realistic weight and authority, the 611's prove that sometimes, in hi-fi, you get what you pay for'. Audition them for yourself soon at most reputable audio stores or contact us directly for more details. And start listening with the A-T shape that's never ever 'square'.

Models available from £12.95 at most good hi-fi stores

	ATH-609	ATH-610	ATH-611
FREQUENCY RESPONSE:	20-20,000 Hz	20-22,000 Hz	20-23,000 Hz
IMPEDANCE / SENSITIVITY:	32 Ohms / 88dB SPL	40 Ohms / 94dB SPL	40 Ohms / 96dB SPL
DRIVER DIAMETER / DIAGHRAGM THICKNESS:	40mm / 25 microns	44mm / 16 microns	44mm / 16 microns

ATH 609 - Open Back
ATH 610 - Closed Back monitor
ATH 611 - Open Back

audio-technica®
□ INNOVATION □ PRECISION □ INTEGRITY

Technica House, Lockwood Close, LEEDS LS11 5UU. *SALES: (0532) 771441 FAX: (0532) 704836*

Brian Ferneyhough

H.K. Gruber

York Höller

Magnus Lindberg

115

MOZART'S LEGACY

HAS LASTED 200 YEARS.

SO COULD YOURS.

When Mozart died in 1791, he left a legacy
of masterpieces. But he wrote no will.

When putting *your* affairs in order, please
consider a legacy towards vital medical
research, benefiting all age groups.

You might give more pleasure than Mozart.

ACTION
RESEARCH
Leading medical research for children

**For a legacy leaflet and more information, please call us (free) on 0800 521533
or write to Action Research, Dept. PG, FREEPOST, Horsham, West Sussex RH12 2BR.**

Charity Number 208701

Janet Owen Thomas

CLIVE BARDA

Steve Reich

GUY VIVIEN

Iannis Xenakis

117

One week after the Last Night, welcome back to the Hall for …

'… SEATED ONE DAY … an only partly serious review of organists and organs (and singers in passing) from ancient Greek times to the present day …' in memory of the Hall's Organist for over 50 years (1934–87), the late **Sir George Thalben-Ball.**

Performers include:

THE BACH CHOIR · HUDDERSFIELD CHORAL SOCIETY · THE RAH ORGAN THE RCM ORCHESTRA · SIR DAVID WILLCOCKS · BRIAN KAY · JOHN SCOTT THOMAS TROTTER · SAINT CECILIA · DAVID SANGER · JONATHAN RENNERT FRANCIS JACKSON · SIMON LINDLEY · PROFESSOR KTESIBIOS · ANDREW LUMSDEN · KEVIN BOWYER · GORDON STEWART · A BRITISH AIRWAYS EMPLOYEE · PETER WRIGHT · IAN CURROR · ADRIAN LUCAS · J.S. BACH DUETTISTS McVICKER & BARHAM · CHRISTOPHER MOORE · ANDREW MORRIS · CÉSAR FRANCK · STEPHEN LAYTON and many more …

Music by Thalben-Ball, Parry, Berlioz, Wagner, Bach, etc.
The audience will be invited to participate in a commissioned work by Robert Stewart

The concert has been planned to raise funds for the Sir George Thalben-Ball Memorial Trust Appeal, whose initial aim is to finance scholarships and bursaries for young organists. All the artists are most generously giving their services.

Tickets available from the Box Office throughout the Proms season. Special rates for parties of 10 or over.

FRIDAY 20 SEPTEMBER 7.30pm
ROYAL ALBERT HALL
Chief Executive Patrick Deuchar

Oxford Music at the Proms

20 July
WILLIAM WALTON: Crown Imperial
RALPH VAUGHAN WILLIAMS: Symphony No. 8

1 August
GRACE WILLIAMS: Sea Sketches

3 August
WILLIAM WALTON: Viola Concerto

12 August
MARTIN BUTLER: O Rio
(world première of BBC commission)

28 August
WILLIAM WALTON: Belshazzar's Feast

29 August
WILLIAM WALTON: Symphony No. 1

Oxford University Press also represents:

Gerald Barry — Michael Berkeley — John Buller — Gordon Crosse
Michael Finnissy — John Gardner — Edward Harper — R Sherlaw Johnson
Constant Lambert — Gordon McPherson — William Mathias
Anthony Powers — Alan Rawsthorne — John Rutter — Phyllis Tate

For further information, please contact Maureen Beedle, Repertoire Promotion Manager, Oxford University Press,
7–8 Hatherley Street, London SW1P 2QT   Telephone: 071 233 5455

BBC SYMPHONY CHORUS

the people below get to sing at the Proms

and at other major concerts

under famous conductors

in music from Beethoven to Berio,

Handel to Henze

and all their concerts are broadcast

on Radio 3

why not join them?

To apply for an audition,
write to:

**BBC Chorus Manager
16 Langham Street
London W1A 1AA**

or telephone **071-927 4370**
at any time

*'The BBC Symphony Chorus,
whose freshness of tone
and vigorous attack ... was
impressive in meeting the
contrasting demands of
Beethoven and Stravinsky.'*
The Times

*'All praise to the
BBC (Symphony) Chorus,
who dispatched their parts
in virtuoso, often thrillingly
dramatic manner.'*
Financial Times

Stephen Jackson, Chorus Director of
the BBC Symphony Chorus

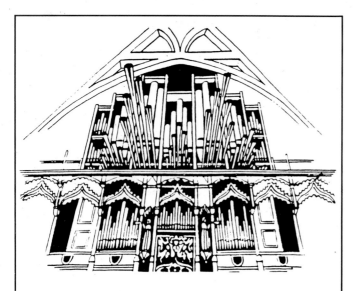

In addition to generous Major and Minor Instrumental Awards and in conjunction with the opening of the New Music School

LORETTO

(HMC Independent Boarding School ages 13–18, girls in Sixth Form)

is offering a major Organ Scholarship for September 1992 at initial or sixth form entry

For further information regarding these and Loretto Piping Bursaries, contact The Admissions Secretary, Loretto, Musselburgh, Midlothian, EH21 7RE Telephone 031-653 2618

Edinburgh 6 miles

INDEX OF ADVERTISERS